# The DIABETIC COOKBOOK

Maxwell Stein

**The Diabetic Cookbook**
Maxwell Stein



Published MMXIV by UKDS,
Hamilton House
Station Road
Epping
CM16 4HA



Typeset by Welland Print Ltd, Spalding, Lincolnshire

**ISBN 978-1-903904-45-9**

# Contents

## Notice To Readers

The contents of this book should never be considered as a substitute for medical advice, and neither should the views, opinions and advice in the following pages be seen as anything other than general information. You should always consult your own doctor – or other fully qualified medical practitioner – for advice and information about any aspects of your health. Additionally, although every effort has been made to ensure the accuracy of the information provided in this publication, neither the author nor the publishers can accept responsibility or liability for that information, this including any of the opinions or advice expressed in the following pages.

# Book One

# Diabetes and Diet

## Optimum Nutrition

More than 1½ million people in the UK have diabetes, and the number is rising year on year. According to health officials, it is caused in part by poor diet, and the increasing incidence of obesity in the young and old. If that is the case, what better reason to write a cookery book that is devoted to healthy recipes for diabetics and for anyone else who wants to eat healthily?

For diabetics, eating a good diet is important, but it does not mean that you will have to eat boring, tasteless food for the rest of your life. In fact, the majority of diabetics find it easy to continue eating their favourite foods, with just a few obvious exclusions. So when your dietician says, "You must go on a special diet", what they really mean is, "Eat a healthy diet so as to keep a healthy balance of insulin levels".

As well as keeping to a healthy diet, eating smaller meals is often more beneficial, and eating at regular intervals will help achieve good blood sugar control. Obviously, you cannot always eat at regular times if you have a busy lifestyle, but if you must skip a meal, substitute a snack as soon as possible.

To live the good life, it is essential that you know a little about nutrition, because the more you understand about the wealth of food choices available, the better for you. When you make healthy choices, your body will feel at its best and your blood glucose is more likely to be under control.

Learn how to count the carbohydrates in your food, so you can live a healthy life. Learn how to avoid saturated fats, refined sugars (which can cause hyperglycaemia), and too much salt. Instead, acquire the knowledge about eating a high fibre diet that includes whole grains, fruits, dairy products, bread and potatoes.

Remember, some foods are better for you than others; there are also some foods that you should try to avoid altogether. It isn't always easy to find exactly the right kind of ingredients when you are shopping, but checking food labels is a useful way of obtaining nutritional information.

## INGREDIENT NOTES

Use unsweetened fruits and juices for diabetic recipes; they can be fresh or tinned, in juice or water-packed. Remember that fruit juice contains carbohydrates and cannot be considered free food for diabetics, so drain all tinned fruits unless specified in the recipe.

Herbs used in diabetic recipes should be dried leaves unless a recipe specifically states ground or fresh. Before adding, be sure to crush leaves in the palm of your hand or with a pestle and mortar to release the flavour.

Be sure to use fresh lemon juice or lime juice in your recipe. Reconstituted lemon and lime juices contain preservatives, and don't taste the same as fresh juice.

Always use fresh garlic in diabetic recipes. Avoid using garlic powder or garlic salt unless the recipe tells you to. Fresh garlic adds distinctive flavour and it's available year-round. More importantly, it possesses healthful properties. It can, in the right circumstances, lower serum cholesterol levels and triglyceride levels. Garlic and onions also contain substances that inhibit blood clots; blood clotting is a major factor in heart attacks and strokes.

## SWEETENERS

In the recipes that follow, refined sugar is avoided wherever possible, and replaced with sweetener. The hazards of refined sugars are obvious, and for most people natural sweeteners will cause fewer problems if used in moderation. It is worth mentioning, however, that the dangers of some sweeteners are many. Diabetics should be very careful replacing sugar with aspartame; it depletes the body of chromium picolinate, which plays a major role in sugar metabolism. Studies have also concluded that the use of aspartame will increase sugar cravings and appetite. This can result in binge eating, which causes weight gain.

Honey is twice as sweet as refined sugar. It does have health benefits: it is used to soothe coughs, and as a treatment for insomnia and nausea. Honey is considered a simple carbohydrate, which is easy to digest. It contains 35% protein, is high in amino acids, digestive enzymes, minerals and vitamins B, C, D and E. It is best to buy the unrefined honey to maintain all these properties. Commercial honey has been heated to 160°C and loses much of its nutrient content. Honey has also been found to contain antioxidant properties; the darker the colour, the higher the antioxidant content.

Molasses is processed from sugar cane. It has many healing properties: it aids in the production of serotonin, it softens the skin, it helps in the treatment of arthritis and uterine fibroids, it expels mucus, and is a good source of iron. It is considered the best choice for a sweetener for most people.

Sucralose or Splenda®, a low-calorie sugar substitute, is made from sugar. It is the newest sweetener on the market. Each teaspoon contains only 2 calories and 1/2g carbohydrate as opposed to the 20 calories and 5g of carbohydrates found in a 5g teaspoon of sugar. The hazards of this sweetener appear to be mild. An overdose can cause loose stools. Splenda¨ can be used cup for cup of sugar. Some recipes may need additional liquid added.

## QUANTITIES

In an effort to bring to you as much variety as possible, the recipes included in this book have been obtained from a wide range of sources from all over the world. However, tastes differ from place to place, as also do measurements for the ingredients. To accommodate these differences, some of the recipes have been adjusted to take into account ingredients not readily available in our shops. The same attention is given to the measurements given for ingredients in recipes, and where possible the measurement has been converted to metric equivalents. Due to these adjustments to ingredients, there might be a slight difference to the nutritional values given in some recipes. For the majority, this should not be cause for concern regarding glucose levels. If, however, you feel there might be a problem, it is advisable to use your own nutritional value calculations when trying out individual recipes.

## DRY MEASURE CONVERSION

| Metric | Imperial | Metric | Imperial |
|---|---|---|---|
| 5g | ⅛ oz | 500 g | 1 lb 2 oz |
| 10 g | ¼ oz | 550 g | 1 lb 4 oz |
| 15 g | ½ oz | 600 g | 1 lb 5 oz |
| 25/30 g | 1 oz | 650 g | 1 lb 7 oz |
| 40 g | 1½ oz | 700 g | 1 lb 9 oz |
| 50 g | 1¾ oz | 750 g | 1 lb 10 oz |
| 60 g | 2¼ oz | 800 g | 1 lb 12 oz |
| 70 g | 2½ oz | 850 g | 1 lb 14 oz |
| 85 g | 3 oz | 900 g | 2 lb |
| 100 g | 3½ oz | 950 g | 2 lb 2 oz |
| 115 g | 4 oz | 1 kg | 2 lb 4 oz |
| 140 g | 5 oz | 1.25 kg | 2 lb 12 oz |
| 150 g | 5½ oz | 1.3 kg | 3 lb |
| 175 g | 6 oz | 1.5 kg | 3 lb 5 oz |

| Metric | Imperial | Metric | Imperial |
|---|---|---|---|
| 200 g | 7 oz | 1.6 kg | 3 lb 8 oz |
| 225 g | 8 oz | 450 g | 1 lb |
| 250 g | 9 oz | 1.8 kg | 4 lb |
| 280 g | 10oz | 2 kg | 4lb 8oz |
| 350 g | 12 oz | 2.25 kg | 5 lb |
| 375 g | 13 oz | 2.5 kg | 5 lb 8 oz |
| 400 g | 14 oz | 2.7 kg | 6 lb |
| 425 g | 15oz | 3 kg | 6lb 8oz |

## FLUID MEASURE CONVERSION

| Metric | Imperial | Metric | Imperial |
|---|---|---|---|
| 15 ml | ½ fl oz | 600 ml | 20 fl oz/ 1 pint |
| 30 ml | 1 fl oz | 700 ml | 1¼ pint |
| 50 ml | 2 fl oz | 850 ml | 1½ pint |
| 75 ml | 2½ fl oz | 1 litre | 1¾ pint |
| 100 ml | 3½ fl oz | 1.2 litres | 2 pint |
| 125 ml | 4 fl oz | 1.4 litres | 2½ pint |
| 150 ml | 5 fl oz/¼ pint | 1.25 ml | ¼ tsp |
| 175 ml | 6 fl oz | 2.5 ml | ½ tsp |
| 200 ml | 7 fl oz/⅓ pint | 5 ml | 1 tsp |
| 225 ml | 8 fl oz | 10 ml | 2 tsp |
| 250 ml | 9 fl oz | 15 ml | 1 tbs/3 tsp |
| 300 ml | 10 fl oz/½ pint | 30 ml | 2 tbs |
| 350 ml | 12 fl oz | 45 ml | 3 tbs |
| 400 ml | 14 fl oz | 60 ml | 4 tbs |
| 425 ml | 15 fl oz/¾ pint | 75 ml | 5 tbs |
| 450 ml | 16 fl oz | 90 ml | 6 tbs |
| 500 ml | 18 fl oz | 95 ml | 7 tbs |

## BRITISH AND AMERICAN WEIGHTS/QUANTITIES

Many people run into difficulties when using recipes from cookbooks specifically intended for consumers in America or in Britain. The main reason, apart from sourcing the ingredients, is the weight/quantity differences used in each country.

The following table is therefore included to show the equivalent weight/quantity for each country.

American measures are classified as either dry measures or fluid measures. Fluid measures are measures of volume, while dry measures are measures of weight. However, do not concern yourself too much whether the ingredient you are measuring is dry or fluid. Simply use the measure that is specified in your recipe. American recipes are almost always in terms of volume.

The Imperial fluid ounce is 4% less than the American fluid ounce.

In practical terms, the size difference of the teaspoon is so small as to be negligible.

The British tablespoon is about 20% larger than an American tablespoon.

1 cup in both systems is a ½ pint measure in their respective systems, but remember there are 20 Imperial fluid ounces in an Imperial pint and only 16 American fluid ounces in an American pint.

| British | American |
|---|---|
| A dash (liquid) | A few drops |
| 1 tablespoon | 1 tablespoon |
| 1½ tablespoons (1fl oz) | 2 tablespoons |
| 2 tablespoons | 3 tablespoons |
| 3 tablespoons (2 fl oz) | ¼ cup |
| 4 tablespoons | ⅓ cup |
| 5 tablespoons | 6 tablespoons |
| 6 tablespoons (4 fl oz) | ½ cup |
| ¼ pint | ⅔ cup |
| 6 floz | ¾ cup |
| ½ pint | 1 cup (8 fl oz) |
| ½ pint | 1¼ cups |
| 1 pint | 2½ cups |

## OVEN TEMPERATURES

Here is a conversion table for common oven temperatures which you may find useful.

| Fahrenheit | Celsius |
|---|---|
| 250°F | 120°C |
| 275°F | 140°C |
| 300°F | 150°C |

| Fahrenheit | Celsius |
|---|---|
| 325°F | 160°C |
| 350°F | 180°C |
| 375°F | 190°C |
| 400°F | 200°C |
| 425°F | 220°C |
| 450°F | 230°C |

## DIETARY EXCHANGES

The principle of Dietary Exchange is based on good nutrition for diabetics and for anyone else interested in keeping to a healthy diet. By dividing foods into 6 different groups we find that it is possible to compile lists of foods that are alike in their composition. The 6 groups are: starch/bread, meat, vegetables, fruits, milk and fats.

The following chart shows the amounts of nutrients in one serving from each exchange list. As you read the exchange lists, you will notice that one choice is often a larger amount of food than another choice from the same list. Because foods are so different, each food is measured or weighed so that the amounts of calories, protein, carbohydrate and fat content are the same in each choice.

## STARCH/BREAD

You can choose your starch exchanges from any of the items on this list. Each item in this list contains:

***Calories: 80 Carbohydrates: 15g Protein: 3g Fats: trace***

***Cereals/Grains/Pasta***

Bran cereals, concentrated
(such as All Bran) ................ ⅓ cup
Bran cereals, flaked.................½ cup
Bulgur wheat(cooked)...............½ cup
Cooked cereals .......................½ cup
Grape Nuts..............................3 tbs
Pasta (cooked) ........................½ cup
Puffed cereal.......................1½ cups
Rice, white or brown (cooked) . ⅓ cup
Shredded wheat ....................½ cup
Wheatgerm .............................3tbs

***Dried Beans/Peas/Lentils***

Beans and peas (cooked):
kidney, white, split, blackeye....⅓ cup
Lentils (cooked)...................... ⅓ cup
Baked beans .........................¼ cup
*Starchy Vegetables*
Corn, sweet............................½ cup
Corn on the cob, 7.5cm ...........1long
Lima beans ............................½ cup
Peas, green (tinned or frozen)....½ cup
Plantain.................................½ cup

Potato, baked 1 small ................75g
Potato, mashed ......................½ cup
Squash, winter
(acorn, butternut) ................. ¾ cup
Yam, sweetpotato .................⅓ cup

***Bread***

Bagel ..............................½ – (25g)
Breadsticks, crisp,
10cm long x 1cm .................2(15g)
Croutons, low-fat......................1cup
English muffin ............................ ½
Frankfurter bun or
hamburger bun .................½ (25g)
Pittabread, 15cm across................½
Plainroll, small.....................1 (25g)
Raisin, unfrosted....................1 slice
White
(including French, Italian) 1 slice (25g)
Wholewheat .........................1slice

***Crackers/Snacks***

Graham crackers ...........................3
Melba toast .........................5 slices
Popcorn (popped, no fat added) ..3 cups
Pretzels ..................................20g
Rye crisp (5cm x 8cm) ................. 4
Wholewheat crackers,
no fat added ...................2–4 (20g)

***Starchy Foods Prepared With Fat***
***(count as 1 starch/bread serving, plus 1 fat serving)***

Biscuit, 6cm across ......................1
Chowmein noodles..................½ cup
Cracker, round butter type ..............6
French – fried potatoes
(5–7.5cm. long) ...............10 (30g)
Muffin, plain, small .......................1
Pancake, 10cm across...................2
Stuffing, bread (prepared) .......¼ cup
Taco shell, 15cm across.................2
Waffle, 10cm square .....................1
Wholewheat crackers,
fat added .......................4–6 (25g)

## MEAT

You can choose your meat exchanges from any of the items on this list. Each item in this list contains:

***Lean***

***Calories: 55 Carbohydrates: 0g Protein: 7g Fats: 0-1g***

Beef–sirloin/tenderloin ...............25g
Pork – fresh ham, tinned, cured,
or boiled bacon, tenderloin .........25g
Veal – all cuts are lean
except for veal cutlets................25g
Poultry – chicken, turkey
(without skin) ..........................25g
Fish – all fresh and frozen fish .....25g
Crab, lobster
(fresh or tinned in water) ..........50g
Scallops, shrimp, clams
(fresh or tinned in water ............50g
Oysters ..........................6 medium
Tuna (tinned in water) ...........¼ cup

Herring .......... 25g
Sardines (tinned) .......... 2 medium
Venison/rabbit .......... 25g
Pheasant, duck, goose (without skin) .......... 25g
Cottage cheese .......... ¼ cup
Grated Parmesan .......... 2tbs
Low-fat cheese (with fewer than 55 calories per 25g) .......... 25g
Egg whites .......... 3
Egg substitutes (with fewer than 55 calories per ¼ cup) .......... ¼ cup

***Medium Fat***

***Calories: 75 Carbohydrates: 0g Protein: 7g Fats: 5g***

Minced beef (rib, chuck, rump), cubed, and meat loaf .......... 25g
Pork chops, loin roast, cutlets .......... 25g
Lamb chops, leg, roast .......... 25g
Veal cutlets (ground or cubed, unbreaded) .......... 25g
Chicken (with skin), ground turkey .......... 25g
Tuna (tinned in oil and drained) ¼ cup
Salmon (tinned .......... ¼ cup
Ricotta cheese .......... ¼ cup
Mozzarella cheese .......... 25g
Egg (high in cholesterol, so limit to 3 per week) .......... 1
Egg substitutes (with 56 – 80 calories per ¼ cup) .......... ¼ cup
Tofu .......... 100g
Liver, heart, kidney (high in cholesterol) .......... 25g

***High Fat***

***Calories: 100 Carbohydrates: 0g Protein: 7g Fats: 8g***

Limit your choices from the high fat group to three times per week. Remember, meat and substitutes do not contribute any fibre to your meal plan.

Prime cuts of beef, corned beef ... 25g
Pork spareribs, minced pork, pork sausages .......... 25g
Lamb, minced .......... 25g
Fish – any fried fish product .......... 25g
Cheddar cheese .......... 25g
Luncheon meat, such as bologna, salami .......... 25g
Sausage meat .......... 25g
Bratwurst .......... 25g
Peanut butter .......... 1tbs

## VEGETABLES

Unless otherwise noted, the serving size for vegetables is 1/2 cup of cooked vegetables or vegetable juice, or 1 cup of raw vegetables

You can choose your vegetable exchanges from any of the items on this list. Each item in this list contains:

***Calories: 25 Carbohydrates: 5g Protein: 0g Fats: 2g***

Artichoke (1/2 medium)
Asparagus
Aubergine
Beans (green, wax, Italian)
Bean sprouts
Beets
Broccoli
Brussels sprouts
Cabbage, cooked
Carrots
Courgettes, cooked
Cauliflower
Rutabaga
Sauerkraut
Spinach, cooked
Summer squash (crookneck)
Greens (collard, mustard, turnip)
Kohlrabi
Leeks
Mushrooms, cooked
Okra
Onions
Pea pods
Peppers (green)
Tomato (one large)
Tomato/vegetable juice
Turnips
Water chestnuts

## FRUIT

Unless otherwise noted, the size for one fruit serving is ½ cup of fresh fruit or fruit juice, or ¼ cup dried fruit.

You can choose your fruit exchanges from any of the items on this list. Each item in this list contains:

***Calories: 60 Carbohydrates: 15g Protein: 0g Fats: 0g***

Apples raw ....................................1
Applesauce (unsweetened) .......½ cup
Apricots (tinned) (4 halves).......½ cup
Banana..........................................½
Blackberries (raw) ..................¾ cup
Cantaloupe (cubes) .................1 cup
Cherries (large, raw) ...........12 whole
Cherries (tinned) .....................½ cup
Figs (raw) ......................................2
Fruit cocktail (tinned) ..............½ cup
Grapefruit (medium) .......................½
Grapefruit (segments) .............¾ cup
Grapes (small) ............................15
Honeydew melon (medium) ..........⅛
Honeydew melon (cubes) .........1 cup
Kiwi (large) ....................................1
Mandarin oranges ..................¾ cup
Mango (small ................................½
Nectarines .....................................1
Orange ..........................................1
Peach ............................................1
Peaches (tinned) (2 halves) ......1 cup
Pear (1/2large) ....................1 small
Pears (tinned) (2halves) ..........½ cup
Pineapple (raw) .....................¾ cup
Pineapple (tinned) ................. ⅓ cup
Plum (raw) ....................................2
Raspberries (raw) ....................1 cup
Strawberries (raw, whole) .....1¼ cups
Tangerine ......................................2
Watermelon (cubes) ............1¼ cups
Apples..................................4 rings
Apricots .............................7 halves
Dates (medium) .........................2½
Figs ..............................................1½
Prunes (medium.............................3
Raisins ..................................2 tbs
Apple juice/cider......................½ cup

Apple juice/cider ....................... ½ cup
Cranberry juice cocktail ........... ⅓ cup
Grapefruit juice ......................... ½ cup
Grape juice ........................... ⅓ cup
Orange juice ............................ ½ cup
Pineapple juice ......................... ½ cup
Prune juice ............................ ⅓ cup

## MILK

You can choose your milk exchanges from any of the items on this list. Each item in this list contains:

***Whole milk***

***Calories: 150 Carbohydrates: 12g Protein: 8g Fats: 8g***

Whole milk .............................. 1 cup
Evaporated whole milk ........... ½ cup
Whole milk plain yoghurt........ 235ml

***Semi-skimmed milk***

***Calories: 120 Carbohydrates: 12g Protein: 8g Fats: 5g***

Semi skimmed milk.................. 1 cup
Plain low-fat yoghurt (with added non-fat milk solids) ................ 235ml

***Skimmed milk***

***Calories: 90 Carbohydrates: 12g Protein: 8g Fats: 0–3g***

Skimmed milk .......................... 1 cup
Low-fat buttermilk..................... 1 cup
Evaporated skimmed milk......... ½ cup
Powdered non-fat milk ............. ⅓ cup
Plain low-fat yoghurt .............. 235ml

## FAT

You can choose your fat exchanges from any of the items on this list. Each item in this list contains:

***Calories: 45 Carbohydrates: 0g Protein: 7g Fats: 5g***

Butter ...................................... 1 tsp
Bacon ...................................... 1 slice
Coconut, shredded ..................... 2 tbs
Coffee whitener, liquid ............... 2 tbs
Coffee whitener, powder............ 4 tsp
Cream (light, coffee, table) ........ 2 tbs
Cream, sour ............................. 2 tbs
Cream (heavy, whipping) ........... 1 tbs
Cream cheese .......................... 1 tbs

## MAKING HEALTHY FOOD CHOICES

Anyone wanting to live a long and healthy life must develop a realistic attitude about what they eat, and make dietary changes if necessary. This will involve looking carefully at the foods consumed and then making healthy food choices.

The Glycaemic Index (GI) helps us to make healthy food choices without having to go without our favourite foods. It is a way of ranking foods on how they affect our blood sugar level. High Glycaemic Index carbohydrates quickly break down in the intestine causing the blood sugar level to rise rapidly; they also elevate insulin levels and stimulate fat storage. Whereas a low Glycaemic Index food will cause a small rise.

A list of carbohydrates with their Glycaemic values is shown below. A number of 70 or more is high, a number of 56 to 69 inclusive is medium, and a number of 55 or less is low.

## THE GLYCAEMIC INDEX OF COMMON FOODS

### *Breads*

Wholemeal bread ....................... 99
White bread ....................... 100
Ryecrisp ....................... 95
Wholegrain rye ....................... 58
Pitta bread ....................... 57
Wholemeal bread ....................... 69
Wholemeal rye bread ....................... 40
100% Stone-ground wholemeal bread ....................... 35

### *Cereals*

Brown rice ....................... 96
Basmati rice ....................... 58
White rice ....................... 83
White spaghetti ....................... 66
Wholewheat spaghetti ....................... 61
Sweetcorn ....................... 87
Puffed Wheat ....................... 80

### *Breakfast cereals*

All Bran ....................... 73
Cornflakes ....................... 119
Muesli ....................... 96
Porridge oats ....................... 85
Shredded wheat ....................... 97
Weetabix ....................... 109
Oatflakes ....................... 40

### *Biscuits*

Digestive biscuits ....................... 82
Oatmeal ....................... 78
Rich Tea ....................... 80
Water biscuits ....................... 91

### *Vegetables*

Frozen peas ....................... 74
Dried green peas ....................... 56
Kidney beans ....................... 54
Romano beans ....................... 65
Red lentils ....................... 43
Chickpeas ....................... 49
Baked beans (tinned) ....................... 60
Butter beans ....................... 52
Haricot beans ....................... 45
Soya beans (dried) ....................... 22
Soya beans (tinned) ....................... 20

### *Root Vegetables*

| Food | GI |
|---|---|
| Potato (instant) | 116 |
| Potato new, boiled | 81 |
| Potato, baked | 135 |
| Potato, sweet | 70 |
| Yam | 74 |
| Carrots, cooked | 85 |
| Beetroot | 65 |

### *Fruit*

| Food | GI |
|---|---|
| Banana | 79 |
| Apple | 53 |
| Cherries | 32 |
| Grapefruit | 36 |
| Grapes | 62 |
| Orange | 66 |
| Orange juice | 67 |
| Peach | 40 |
| Pears | 47 |
| Plums | 34 |
| Raisins | 93 |

### *Sugars*

| Food | GI |
|---|---|
| Fructose | 30 |
| Glucose | 138 |
| Honey | 126 |
| Maltose | 152 |
| Sucrose | 86 |

### *Dairy Products*

| Food | GI |
|---|---|
| Skimmed milk | 46 |
| Wholemilk | 49 |
| Ice cream | 52 |
| Yoghurt | 52 |

The above statistics have been arrived at from Glycaemic Indices prepared from difference sources throughout the world. It was noted that the Glycaemic Index of some food products differs slightly in value according to where the foods have been grown or produced. As a result, every attempt has been made to list only products that have a similar Glycaemic Index value in each country.

# Part Two

# Diabetic Recipes From Around The World

# Introduction

## COOKING METHODS

Cooking the food you have bought may mean you need to adapt your recipes and how you cook. There are things you can do to lower fat and cholesterol, lower salt (sodium), lower sugar, and increase fibre.

## SALT

Depending too much on salt when cooking makes it easy to overlook other flavourings. Next time something needs seasoning during cooking, try one of these:

Black pepper, buttermilk, vegetable flavouring, chilli, finely chopped onion, garlic, herbs, horseradish, lemon rind and juice, mustard, paprika, plain low-fat yoghurt, toasted almonds, and tomato purée.

## MEAT

Try to avoid frying and braising meats. Instead try grilling for a change. Do not add flour, breadcrumbs, coating mixes, or fat to dishes unless the recipe expressly calls for them. Trim off fat before cooking or serving meat dishes. Weigh meat after removing bones and fat and again after cooking.

The meaty taste in casserole dishes is often enhanced by being prepared in advance then reheated when required. This process tenderises the meat and allows flavours to intermingle.

## VEGETABLES

- Vegetables should be boiled or steamed, unless the recipe specifically says 'stir-fry', in which case the fat content will be taken into account for that meal.
- Fresh herbs can be frozen unblanched separate from their stalks in small

polythene bags or containers. Crumble into the dish while still frozen – there is no need to thaw and chop.

- Keep a special board for slicing or crushing cloves of garlic. This way you will avoid contaminating other foods with the taste of garlic.
- Root vegetables can be prepared several hours before they are required. Simply cover them in a basin of water to which salt or lemon juice has been added to stop them from discolouring.
- To skin grapes or tomatoes, plunge them into boiling water for a few minutes, and then quickly transfer them to cold water.
- To restore the fresh taste in frozen vegetables, pour boiling water over them as soon as they come out of the freezer.
- Keep root vegetables fresher longer by removing the tops as soon as you can.
- Stuffed vegetables are a perfect way to get lots of flavour and texture into one simple dish. These foods can contain a variety of ingredients necessary for a nourishing, well-balanced meal. Favourite vegetables to stuff are courgettes, onions, capsicum, and tomatoes.
- Cut courgettes lengthwise and use a teaspoon with a pointed tip to scrape out the soft, seedy centre into a wide, deep channel. Add enough filling to cover the entire surface.
- Beef tomatoes are best type for stuffing. Cut the fruit in half, then simply scoop out the seeds, and pack in the filling.
- Onions need to be boiled for a couple of minutes before stuffing. Use a melon baller to scoop out the inside, leaving a shell two layers thick. Stuff the onions with your choice of filling and bake.
- Capsicum (sweet peppers), make perfect containers for the stuffing of your choice. Just slice off the top and remove the white flesh and seeds from inside. They have a mild, sweet flavour and crisp, juicy flesh.

# Vegetarian Lasagne

**Serves: 6**

**Nutritional value per serving**

Calories: 250 Fat: 6g Carbohydrate: 31g

Protein: 19.5g Dietary Fibre: 4g

## Ingredients

- 225g lasagne verdi (16 sheets 18 x 7.5cm)
- 250g broccoli
- 1 x 340g tin chopped plum tomatoes, juice included
- 1 stick celery, sliced
- 1 onion, sliced
- 1 green pepper, roughly chopped
- 1½ tsp dried basil
- 2 bay leaves
- 3 cloves garlic, crushed
- 2 cups fat free ricotta cheese
- 100g shredded part-skim mozzarella cheese
- salt and black pepper to season
- 1 tbs freshly grated Parmesan cheese

Steam the broccoli for 10 minutes then allow to cool. Meanwhile cook the lasagne in fresh boiling water until tender; drain well and set aside.

Place the tomatoes, celery, onion, pepper, basil, bay leaves, garlic and salt in a large saucepan and bring to boiling point; reduce the heat and simmer, uncovered, for 25 minutes or until the juices have thickened; stir occasionally to prevent sticking to the bottom of the pan. Discard the bay leaves.

Stir together the ricotta cheese, Parmesan cheese and black pepper; then stir in the cooked broccoli.

Spread about a quarter of the sauce in a greased 18 x 24cm roasting tin, then arrange a single layer of the lasagne over the top. Repeat this process, finishing off with a final layer of sauce.

Bake, uncovered, in a preheated oven at 180°C for 30-35 minutes; sprinkle with mozzarella. Bake about 5 minutes more until the cheese has melted. Let stand 10 minutes before serving.

•

# Gazpacho

**Serves: 2**

**Nutritional value per serving**

Calories: 37 Fat: 0.5g Carbohydrate: 8g

Protein: 1.5g Dietary Fibre: 1.6g

## Ingredients

3 large tomatoes, coarsely chopped
1 red pepper, coarsely chopped
1 medium cucumber, coarsely chopped
1 small onion, coarsely chopped
4 cloves garlic, crushed
1 piece bread, broken into pieces
1 cup fresh water
½ tsp cumin
¼ tsp paprika
4 tbs red wine
1 tsp salt
¼ tsp ground black pepper, to taste

Combine all the vegetables and bread in a food processor until they are roughly blended. Chill in the refrigerator for about an hour before serving.

•

# Spiced Rice Pilaf

**Serves: 6**

**Nutritional value per serving**

Calories: 176 Fat: 5g Carbohydrate: 31g

Protein: 3g Dietary Fibre: 1g

## Ingredients

1 cup brown basmati rice
3 tsp olive oil
1 small onion chopped
3 cloves garlic, crushed
3 cloves, chopped
2 cups chicken stock
1 cinnamon stick
1 tbs raisins

| 1 tbs pine nuts |
|---|

Heat 2 teaspoons of oil in a large non-stick saucepan, and sauté the onion and garlic until translucent.

Add the cloves and cook for 1 minute. Add the rice and stir to coat. Add the stock and the cinnamon stick; bring to boil, cover and simmer for 20 to 25 minutes, until the liquid is absorbed. Discard the cinnamon stick.

Heat the remaining teaspoon of oil in a small frying pan; add the raisins and pine nuts, and cook over a medium heat for 1 minute.

Serve the Pilaf with the raisin and pine nuts sprinkled over the top.

•

# Mixed Vegetables Gratin

**Serves: 4**

**Nutritional value per serving**

Calories: 137 | Fat: 4g | Carbohydrate: 20g

Protein: 7g | Dietary Fibre: 5g

## Ingredients

| 3 carrots, peeled and sliced |
|---|
| 110g cauliflower florets |
| 110g broccoli florets |
| 110g sweetcorn |
| 1 medium size onion, finely chopped |

## Herb Sauce

| 3 tbs skimmed milk |
|---|
| 1 tsp cornflour |
| 2 tbs cheddar cheese |
| 1 tsp Dijon mustard |
| 2 tsp mixed herbs |
| coarsely ground pepper for seasoning |

## Topping

| 2 tbs finely grated Cheddar cheese |
|---|
| 2 ripe tomatoes, sliced lengthwise |
| 50g dry breadcrumbs |

Steam the carrots, cauliflower and broccoli for 10 minutes, or until just tender.

Place in a large, ovenproof dish, cover and keep warm.

For the herb sauce, mix together the sauce ingredients in a small saucepan. Warm over a low heat, stirring until it begins to thicken.

Pour the sauce over the vegetables and mix gently. Top with the grated cheese and tomato slices. Serve immediately.

•

## Boston Rice Medley

**Serves: 4**

**Nutritional value per serving**

Calories: 195 | Fat: 0g | Carbohydrate: 43g

Protein: 5g | Dietary Fibre: 1g

### Ingredients

- 475ml chicken stock
- 180g American long-grain rice
- ½ tsp turmeric
- 25g seedless raisins
- 4 spring onions, thinly sliced
- 25g pine kernels, roasted

Heat the chicken stock in a medium size saucepan until boiling; add the rice and turmeric and cook for 15 to 20 minutes, or until the liquid is absorbed and the rice is tender.

Remove from the heat and add the raisins, pine kernels and spring onions. Stir the rice to mix together. Serve hot.

•

## Hummus Paste

**Serves: 4**

**Nutritional value per serving**

Calories: 70 | Fat: 6g | Carbohydrates: 8g

Protein: 5g | Dietary Fibre: 1g

### Ingredients

- 450g chickpeas, cooked
- 2 tbs lemon juice
- ¼ cup toasted sesame seeds

1 small onion, finely chopped
3 cloves garlic, crushed
2 tsp olive oil
2 tsp ground cumin
¼ tsp cayenne pepper
¼ tsp salt
1 tbs fresh parsley, finely chopped for garnish

Combine all the ingredients, except the parsley, in a blender. Purée until smooth, adding a little liquid if needed to thin the purée. Refrigerate for 3–6 hours before serving to blend the flavours.

Garnish with parsley before serving with vegetables, pitta bread or as a sandwich spread.

•

# Potato Croquettes

**Serves: 5**

**Nutritional value per (2 croquettes)**

| Calories: 90 | Fat: 0g | Carbohydrate: 18g |
|---|---|---|
| Protein: 2g | Dietary Fibre: 2g | |

## Ingredients

1 large potato, cooked and mashed
1 medium size parsnips, cooked and mashed
¼ tsp ground cinnamon
¼ tsp nutmeg

## For the coating

1 small egg, beaten
breadcrumbs, as required

Mix together the potato, parsnips and ground spices in a mixing bowl.

Shape the mixture into small croquettes about 4cm long, then place in a refrigerator for 25 minutes to chill. When ready, roll each croquette in the beaten egg, then in the breadcrumbs.

Place in an ovenproof dish. Bake in a preheated oven at 180°C, uncovered, for 30 minutes.

•

## Spanish Paella

**Serves: 6**

**Nutritional value per serving**

Calories: 610 Fat: 25.2g Carbohydrate: 60g

Protein: 36g Dietary Fibre: 4.2g

### Ingredients

- 2 chicken thigh fillets, diced
- 2 tbs olive oil
- 1 tsp paprika
- 2 cups basmati rice
- 4 cups chicken stock
- 400g tin chopped tomatoes
- 1 red pepper, deseeded and roughly chopped
- 200g fresh or frozen peas
- 6 medium size prawns, peeled, heads/ shells removed
- 1 onion, roughly chopped

Sauté the diced chicken until golden brown on all sides; add the onion and continue to cook until the onion is translucent. Stir in the rice and tomatoes; keep stirring until mixed well with the chicken and onions. Add the stock and then season with the paprika. Cover and simmer for 20 minutes.

Add the pepper, peas and prawns. Cook for a further 10 minutes or until the liquid has thickened and the rice is tender. Serve hot with chunks of crusty bread.

•

## Ratatouille

**Serves 4**

**Nutritional value per serving**

Calories: 4 Fat: 5g Carbohydrate: 19g

Protein: 123g Dietary Fibre: 6.4g

### Ingredients

- 1 small aubergine, cut into 2cm cubes
- salt and freshly ground black pepper
- 2 tbs extra virgin olive oil
- 2 large red peppers, deseeded and cut into 2cm pieces

4 small courgettes, sliced
1 onion, coarsely chopped
4 cloves garlic, minced
450g tomatoes, chopped
1 tbs chopped fresh basil

Sprinkle the aubergine lightly with salt and let it drain in a colander for 30 minutes.

Using a large saucepan, heat 1 tablespoon of oil over a medium-high heat. Add the aubergine and cook until soft and brown, stirring all the time. Transfer the aubergine to a bowl and place on one side.

Pour the remaining oil into the saucepan and heat. When hot, add the peppers, courgettes, onion and garlic. Continue cooking, stirring all the time until tender.

Mix in the tomatoes, basil and aubergine, stirring occasionally. Cook over a low heat for 15 to 20 minutes, or until all the vegetables are tender; season with salt and pepper to taste.

Serve hot or cold as a side dish, or over rice for an entrée.

•

## Turkey Mince in Sauce

**Serves: 4**

**Nutritional value per serving**

Calories: 290 | Fat: 2g | Carbohydrate: 31g
Protein: 38g | Dietary Fibre: 9g

### Ingredients

450g minced turkey breast
1 tbs olive oil
1 x 340g tin pinto beans, drained and rinsed
350ml low-salt chicken stock
1 x 340g tin chopped tomatoes
1 tbs tomato paste
1 tsp Worcestershire sauce
1 tsp soy sauce
1 tbs chilli powder
¼ tsp ground cinnamon
¼ tsp ground cumin
½ tsp fresh ground pepper

Brown the turkey until it is no longer pink; drain off any excess fat. Add the remaining ingredients and continue cooking until boiling. Lower the heat and simmer for 20 minutes.

Serve with pasta or on a bed of rice.

•

## Potato Patties

**Serves: 4**

**Nutritional value per serving**

Calories: 85 | Fat: 1g | Carbohydrate: 15g

Protein: 3g | Dietary fibre: 2g

### Ingredients

- 2 medium size potatoes, peeled
- 3 tbs skimmed milk
- 50g frozen spinach, thawed
- 1 small onion, finely chopped
- ½ tsp garlic powder
- black pepper for seasoning
- 1 tsp olive oil
- 2 tbs cheddar cheese

Slice the potatoes and steam until tender; about 15-20 minutes. Remove from the heat when cooked and allow to cool. Place the potatoes and milk in a mixing bowl and mash to a smooth texture.

Stir in the spinach, onion and garlic salt, and season with black pepper; stir to mix well. Remove the mixture from the bowl onto a floured kitchen board; divide and shape the mixture into 4 patties.

Cook the patties for 8-10 minutes in a frying pan over medium-high heat. Turn the patties over half way through cooking so that they are browned on both sides.

Serve hot with grated cheese sprinkled over the top.

•

## Peppered Green Beans

**Serves: 7**

**Nutritional value per serving**

Calories: 30 | Fat: 1g | Carbohydrate: 4g

Protein: 1g | Dietary Fibre: 1g

### Ingredients

320g fresh green beans, topped and tailed

### For the Marinade

2 tbs fresh chopped chives
2 tbs white wine vinegar
1 tbs balsamic vinegar
2 tsp olive oil
1 tsp cayenne pepper

Combine all the marinade ingredients until well mixed.

Boil the green beans for 10 to 15 minutes until tender-crisp. Drain in a colander and pour cold water over to prevent further cooking.

Arrange the beans in a serving dish and pour the marinade over the top. Leave to marinate for 30 minutes before serving.

•

## Stir-fry Water Chestnuts with Sprouts

**Serves: 4**

**Nutritional value per serving**

Calories: 99 | Fat: 3g | Carbohydrate: 18g
Protein: 3g | Dietary fibre: 2g

### Ingredients

450g Brussels sprouts, cooked, sliced in halves
2 tsp olive oil
1 tin water chestnuts, drained and sliced in halves
½ cup chicken stock
3 spring onions, finely chopped
salt and pepper

Heat the oil in a wok, add the chestnuts and sprouts, and stir-fry for 2 to 3 minutes.

Add the stock to the wok and cook, covered, for a further minute or two. Season with salt and pepper and continue cooking for another minute.

Garnish with chopped spring onions before serving.

•

# Lentil and Vegetable Stir-fry

**Serves: 4**

**Nutritional value per serving**

Calories: 115 Fat: 4g
Protein: 9g Dietary Fibre: 1g

## Ingredients

- 1 cup red lentils
- 3 cups chicken stock
- 1 bay leaf
- ¼ tsp marjoram
- ¼ tsp thyme
- 1 tsp olive oil
- 3 head of bak-choi Chinese cabbage, sliced
- 1 stalk of celery, sliced
- 6 spring onions, sliced
- 1 small tin water chestnuts, sliced
- 2 tbs balsamic vinegar

Rinse the lentils and place in a saucepan with the stock, bay leaf, marjoram and thyme. Heat until boiling, then reduce the heat and simmer, uncovered, for 30 minutes or until the lentils are tender. Drain in a colander.

Heat the oil in a non-stick saucepan and stir-fry the vegetables for 3 minutes. Add the lentils, hot pepper, water chestnuts and balsamic vinegar. Serve on a bed of lettuce leaves.

•

# Stir-Fried Courgettes

**Serves: 4**

**Nutritional value per serving**

Calories: 90 Fat: 6g Carbohydrate: 8g
Protein: 2g Dietary Fibre: 2g

## Ingredients

- 1 tbs olive oil
- 450g courgettes, sliced
- 1 onion, cut into thin wedges
- ½ tsp grated fresh ginger
- 1 tbs sesame seeds

| |
|---|
| 1 tbs light soy sauce |
| 1½ tsp sesame oil |
| ½ tsp Chinese five spice |

Heat the oil in a wok over a medium heat. Add the courgettes, onion and ginger. Stir-fry until the courgettes and onions are crisp on the outside. Sprinkle with sesame seeds, soy sauce, five spice and sesame oil. Toss to combine all the ingredients.

•

## Sweet Potato Wedges

**Serves: 4**

**Nutritional value per serving**

Calories: 71 Fat: 0.5g Carbohydrate: 17g

Protein: 1g Dietary Fibre: 2g

### Ingredients

| |
|---|
| 250g sweet potatoes, peeled and sliced into thin wedges |
| Freshly ground black pepper for seasoning |

Place the potato wedges in a single layer on a greased baking sheet. Brush the wedges with olive oil; then sprinkle with pepper.

Roast in a preheated oven at 190°C for 40 minutes turning once to brown all over.

•

## German Pasta with Red Cabbage

**Serves: 6**

**Nutritional value per serving**

Calories: 110 Fat: 2g Carbohydrate: 22g

Protein: 3g Dietary Fibre: 2g

### Ingredients

| |
|---|
| 100g pasta, cooked |
| 2 tsp vegetable oil |
| 300g red cabbage, shredded |
| 1 tbs sweetener |

| 2 tbs red wine vinegar |
|---|
| 1 tsp caraway seed |
| freshly milled black pepper for seasoning |

Heat the oil in a large pan; add the cabbage and stir-fry for 2 minutes. Stir in the sweetener, vinegar and caraway seed.

Cover and cook for about 5 minutes, stirring occasionally, until crisp-tender. Stir in the pasta; heat until hot. Season with freshly milled pepper.

•

# Potato Spinach Quiche

**Serves: 6**

**Nutritional value per serving**

Calories: 121 Fat: 4g Carbohydrate: 9g

Protein: 13g Dietary Fibre: 2g

## Ingredients

| 300g frozen chopped spinach, thawed |
|---|
| 120ml low-fat plain yoghurt |
| 1 medium size potato, sliced |
| 3 spring onions, finely sliced |
| ¼ tsp nutmeg |
| freshly ground black pepper for seasoning |

Using a mixing bowl, combine the spinach with the yoghurt, egg substitute, spring onions and nutmeg; then season with pepper.

Transfer the mixture into a non-stick 22cm ovenproof pie dish and place the potato slices in a single layer over the top.

Bake the quiche in a preheated oven at 180°C for 35-40 minutes, or until the potatoes are browned on top.

•

# Spanish Vegetable Paella

**Serves: 6**

**Nutritional value per serving**

Calories: 294 Fat: 2g Carbohydrate: 59g

Protein: 8g Dietary Fibre: 3g

## Ingredients

- 2 tsp olive oil
- 1 red onion, chopped
- 1 small red pepper, chopped
- 1 small green pepper, chopped
- 1 small courgette, sliced
- 75g yellow squash, diced
- 1 x 340g tin chopped tomatoes
- 370g basmati rice
- 750ml vegetable stock
- pinch of saffron threads
- freshly ground pepper and salt for seasoning

Sauté the onion, courgette and yellow squash in hot oil for 5 minutes; add the carrots and tomatoes and bring to a boil. Reduce the heat and simmer for 5 minutes. Season with salt and pepper.

Add the remaining ingredients; turn up the heat until the stock begins to boil, then turn down and simmer for 20 minutes, or until the rice is tender.

•

# Roast Mediterranean Vegetables

**Serves: 4**

**Nutritional value per serving**

Calories: 63 Fat: 4g Carbohydrate: 8g

Protein: 1g Dietary Fibre: 3g

## Ingredients

- 1 tbs olive oil
- 1 clove garlic, crushed
- ½ tsp dried rosemary
- 2 courgettes, sliced
- 1 red pepper, coarsely chopped
- 1 green pepper, coarsely chopped
- 1 small aubergine, coarsely chopped
- 2 red onions, coarsely chopped

Combine the olive oil, garlic and rosemary in a large mixing bowl; toss the vegetables in the oil until well covered. Place the chopped vegetables in a baking dish, cover with foil and roast in a preheated oven at 180°C for about 20 minutes.

Remove the foil and bake for a further 10 minutes. Season the vegetables before serving.

•

## Broccoli with Pecan Nuts

**Serves: 6**

**Nutritional value per serving**

Calories: 61 | Fat: 2.1g | Carbohydrate: 9g
Protein: 3.7g | Dietary Fibre: 0g

### Ingredients

- 5g knob of butter
- 4 tbs chopped pecan nuts
- ½ tsp dried marjoram
- ¼ tsp dried chervil
- 2 tbs finely chopped parsley
- 700g broccoli, cut into florets
- salt and pepper, to taste

Steam the broccoli for 5 minutes and place to one side.

Melt the butter in a stainless steel saucepan over a medium heat; add the pecan nuts and cook until toasted, stirring frequently.

Add the marjoram and chervil; cook for a further minute, stirring frequently. Remove from the heat and stir in the parsley.

Season the broccoli with salt and pepper, and arrange in a serving bowl. Spoon the pecan nuts and herbs over the broccoli.

•

## French Green Beans with Tomatoes

**Serves: 4**

**Nutritional value per serving**

Calories: 123 | Fat: 4.3g | Carbohydrate: 20.5g
Protein: 4.5g | Dietary Fibre: 2.2g

### Ingredients

- 450g French beans
- 1 red onion, roughly chopped
- 1 x 435g tin chopped plum tomatoes with liquid

- 4 cloves garlic, finely sliced
- 1 tbs olive oil
- ¾ tsp dried oregano
- ½ tsp dried basil
- salt and pepper, to taste

Heat the oil in a large pan, add the onion and garlic; sauté until translucent. Stir in the herbs and cook for one to two minutes longer.

Add the beans and tomatoes; heat to boiling point, and then reduce the heat and simmer, covered, until the beans are tender.

Season with salt and pepper.

•

# Spiced Vegetables from Pakistan

**Serves: 8**

**Nutritional value per serving**

Calories: 69 Fat: 1g Carbohydrate: 15g

Protein: 2g Dietary Fibre: 3g

## Ingredients

- 2 tbs olive oil
- 2 cloves garlic, crushed
- 1 large onion, sliced
- 3 beef tomatoes, coarsely chopped
- 1 cup precooked chickpeas
- 3 Charlotte potatoes, cut into halves
- ¼ tsp ground cloves
- ¼ tsp ground turmeric
- ½ tsp cinnamon
- ½ tsp ground chilli
- ½ tsp red pepper flakes
- 2 tsp cumin

Heat the oil in a large saucepan, add the onions and garlic; sauté until translucent. Add all the spices and tomatoes and stir until combined. Stir in the remaining vegetables, cover with a tight lid and leave to cook for 15 minutes or until the vegetables are cooked. Stir occasionally.

•

# French Onion Pie

**Serves: 6**

**Nutritional value per serving**

Calories: 68 | Fat: 4g | Carbohydrate: 7g
Protein: 2g | Dietary Fibre: 1g

## Ingredients

- 2 tbs olive oil
- 3 large onions, finely chopped
- 4 cloves of garlic, crushed
- 1 cup skimmed milk
- 275g cubed tofu, crumbled
- pinch of nutmeg
- 2 tbs plain flour
- 1 tbs couscous
- freshly milled black pepper for seasoning
- 1 unbaked pie shell

Heat the oil in a large saucepan, add the onions and garlic; sauté until translucent.

Blend the tofu, milk, nutmeg and flour in a mixing bowl until smooth. Combine with the onions and garlic, and add the couscous.

Pour the blended ingredients into a 22cm pie shell and season with pepper. Bake in a preheated oven at 180°C for 30 minutes.

•

# Malayan Broccoli Noodles

**Serves: 4**

**Nutritional value per serving**

Calories: 328 | Fat: 8g | Carbohydrate: 51g
Protein: 15g | Dietary Fibre: 3g

## Ingredients

- 225g egg noodles
- 2 bunches spring onions
- 2 cloves of garlic, crushed
- 2 tbs peeled minced fresh ginger
- 2 tbs soy sauce

- sweetener, equivalent to 1 tbs sugar
- 3 tbs vegetable stock
- 2 tbs fresh lime juice
- 8 large broccoli florets
- 1 tbs olive oil

Cook the egg noodles according to package instructions, drain and rinse with cold water; then set aside.

Combine the spring onions with the garlic, ginger, soy sauce and sweetener; add the stock and lime juice.

Stir-fry the broccoli in hot oil until tender; add the drained noodles and stock, stirring constantly to heat evenly throughout.

Serve hot.

•

## Corn on the Cob

**Serves: 6**

**Nutritional value per serving**

Calories: 79 | Fat: 0.5g | Carbohydrate: 18g

Protein: 3g | Dietary Fibre: 3g

### Ingredients

- 6 cobs of corn, husked
- chilli powder for seasoning
- butter, as required

Plunge the cobs into boiling water and leave to simmer for 10 minutes. Test the kernels for tenderness with a skewer, and then drain well.

Serve with a dressing of butter and a sprinkling of chilli powder.

•

## Spanish Garlic Eggs

**Serves: 6**

**Nutritional value per serving**

Calories: 385 | Fat: 36.5g | Carbohydrate: 3.4g

Protein: 11.4g | Dietary Fibre: 0.7g

### Ingredients

12 eggs, hard boiled
1 handful fresh parsley
4 cloves garlic
½ tsp paprika
¼ tsp black pepper
¾ cup olive oil
1 small carrot (grated)
4 green olives, stoned and sliced
4 black olives, stoned and sliced

Allow the eggs to cool, and then peel off the shells and cut into quarters. Arrange in a serving dish and put to one side.

Make a dressing with the parsley, garlic, paprika and black pepper by placing the ingredients in a blender and whisking on high until all the ingredients are combined. Turn the blender to low speed and slowly add the olive oil. Drizzle ¾ of the dressing over the eggs, reserving ¼ of the oil for later.

Garnish the eggs with the grated carrot and sliced green and black olives, and then drizzle the remaining dressing over the garnished eggs. Cover and refrigerate for at least 2 hours before serving.

•

## Baked French Fries

**Serves: 2**

### Nutritional value per serving

Calories: 93 Fat: 3g Carbohydrate: 15g
Protein: 2g Dietary Fibre: 1.8g

### Ingredients

2 large potatoes
1 tbs vegetable oil

Wash and peel the potatoes and cut into chips 10cm long and 1cm wide. Rinse under fresh water then place in a bowl of iced water to crisp for ½ hour.

When ready to cook, shake off excess water and pat dry on a kitchen towel.

To cook, spread the chips in one layer on a shallow baking tray. Sprinkle with vegetable oil then shake the tray to spread the oil evenly over the chips.

Bake the chips in a preheated oven at 180ºC for 30-40 minutes, turning frequently, until gold brown.

When cooked, remove any excess oil by placing the chips onto paper towels before serving. Season as required.

•

## Baked Organic Potato Skins

**Serves: 2**

**Nutritional value per serving**

Calories: 55 Carbohydrates: 9g Fat: 0.3g

Protein: 5g Dietary Fibre: 1.2g

### Ingredients

| |
|---|
| 2 medium size organic potatoes |
| 25g grated fat-free cheddar cheese |
| sprinkling of crispy bacon |
| 4 spring onions, finely sliced |
| olive oil, as required |

Scrub the potatoes and pierce each with a fork. Bake in a preheated oven at 220ºC until soft; about 1 hour. Alternatively, microwave for 5 or 6 minutes, or until cooked.

Cut the potatoes in half lengthwise and scoop out the centres, leaving a 5mm thick shell. (Reserve removed potato for another use.) Cut potato halves lengthwise then lightly coat with olive oil.

Place on a large baking sheet and bake in a preheated oven at 220ºC for 15-20 minutes, or until brown and crisp.

When ready, sprinkle evenly with cheese, crispy bacon and spring onions. Place under a hot grill and brown for 3 minutes to melt the cheese.

•

## Mexican Beans in Tomato Sauce

**Serves: 8**

**Nutritional value per serving**

Calories: 228 Fat: 4.4g Carbohydrates: 37.9g

Protein: 11.7g Dietary Fibre: 1g

## Ingredients

| |
|---|
| 2 cups dry pinto beans |
| 1 medium onion, coarsely chopped |
| 1 medium poblano chilli, chopped |
| 1 medium red pepper, chopped |
| 4 cloves garlic, crushed |
| 1 tbs ginger root, finely chopped |
| 2 serrano chillies, finely chopped |
| 2 tbs olive oil |
| 3 tsp chilli powder |
| 2 tsp dried oregano leaves |
| 1 tsp ground cumin |
| ½ tsp cayenne pepper |
| 1 large tin chopped plum tomatoes with juice |

Rinse the beans in cold water then place in a large saucepan and add enough fresh water to cover the beans.

Cook the beans over a high heat until the water has reached boiling point; leave for a few minutes then turn off the heat and let the saucepan stand, covered, for 1 hour; then drain off the water.

Heat the oil in a pan, and when hot sauté the onion, poblano chilli, pepper, garlic, ginger root and serrano chillies until tender. Stir in the chopped tomatoes, chilli powder, herbs and cayenne pepper; cook for a further 5 minutes, or until the tomatoes are tender.

Serve the beans with the hot tomato sauce poured over the top.

•

# Stuffed Peppers

**Serves: 4**

**Nutritional value per serving**

Calories: 250 | Total Fat: 5g | Carbohydrate: 30g

Protein: 20g | Dietary Fibre: 5g

## Ingredients

| |
|---|
| 4 equally sized sweet peppers, tops, ribs and seeds removed |
| 225g ground chicken breast |
| 325g cooked brown rice |
| 1 small onion, finely chopped |
| 2 cloves garlic, thinly sliced |

150g tinned haricot beans, rinsed and drained
150g frozen sweetcorn, thawed
1 tsp dried parsley
1 tsp dried oregano
sprinkling freshly ground black pepper
sprinkling grated Parmesan cheese
50g whole-grain breadcrumbs

Prepare the capsicum and place on one side.

For the filling, combine all the remaining ingredients, except the cheese and black pepper, in a large bowl. Season with the pepper then mix lightly with a fork so that the beans aren't mashed. Set aside.

Divide the filling into four portions, packing each pepper with the mixture, placing any extra at the top. Place the stuffed peppers in a baking dish just large enough to hold them. Pour in 1 cup of water and then cover the dish with foil and bake it in the centre of a preheated oven at 220°C for 40 minutes.

When ready, sprinkle the Parmesan cheese over the top of each pepper. Continue baking the peppers, uncovered, for 15 minutes, or until the peppers are soft when pierced with a knife, but not collapsing. Place on a serving dish and serve.

•

## Potato Scallops

**Serves: 8**

**Nutritional value per serving**

Calories: 155 | Fat: 6g | Carbohydrate: 20g
Protein: 6g | Dietary Fibre: 2g

### Ingredients

5 medium potatoes, thinly sliced
2 tbs margarine
2 tbs plain flour
2 cups skimmed milk
1 shallot, chopped
1 tbs fresh dill, chopped small
½ tsp dry mustard
sprinkling ground white pepper
75g cheddar cheese, grated

Melt the margarine in a non-stick heavy gauge frying pan. Add the flour and stir over a medium heat until blended. Add the milk and cook, stirring constantly, until the mixture thickens and bubbles.

Stir in the shallot, dill and mustard; season with a sprinkling of pepper and heat for another minute. Remove from the heat.

Arrange the potato slices in an ovenproof dish and pour the sauce over the potatoes. Sprinkle with cheese and cook in a preheated oven at 160°C for 1 hour, or until the potatoes have browned.

•

# Green Bean Casserole

**Serves: 2**

**Nutritional value per serving**

Calories: 52 Fat: 1.5g Carbohydrate: 7.3g

Protein: 3.1g Dietary Fibre: 2.2g

## Ingredients

| |
|---|
| 1 small tin cream of chicken soup |
| 1 tsp soy sauce |
| 1 onion, thinly sliced |
| 750g French green beans, cooked and drained |
| ground black pepper to season |

Stir the soy sauce into the chicken soup then place in a 1 litre oven proof casserole dish.

Mix in the onions and beans then season with pepper.

Bake in a preheated oven at 200°C for 20 minutes or until bubbling.

•

# Kedgeree

**Serves: 4**

**Nutrition Information Per Serving**

Calories: 495 Fat: 24g Carbohydrates: 31g

Protein: 44g Dietary Fibre: 0g

## Ingredients

| |
|---|
| 100g brown rice, cooked and drained dry |
| 1 hard boiled egg |

20g margarine
1 tsp of chopped parsley
125g cold cooked smoked haddock, flaked

Chop the egg white coarsely and mix with the fish. Heat the margarine in a saucepan and when hot add the fish; cook for 1 minute then add the rice; continue cooking for a further 3 minutes.

To serve, heap the kedgeree in an entrée dish in the shape of a pyramid. Garnish with chopped parsley in a long line down the side. Sprinkle the yolk of the egg, rubbed through a sieve over the top. Serve at once.

•

## Thai Wontons

**Serves: 3**

**Nutritional value per serving (4 pieces)**

Calories: 54 | Fat: 2g | Carbohydrate: 8g
Protein: 2g | Dietary Fibre: 1g

### Ingredients

12 wonton wrappers

### Filling

1 tbs smooth peanut butter
½ tbs soy sauce
1 tsp water
½ tsp sesame oil
4 tsp rice wine vinegar
¼ tsp ginger

Warm the peanut butter then mix with all the filling ingredients until a smooth paste is formed.

Spoon the filling onto the wonton wrappers and then fold the corners together to make small parcels.

To cook, arrange the wonton wrappers on a slightly greased baking sheet in a single layer and bake in a preheated oven at 220°C for 3-5 minutes, or until the wontons have crisped.

Allow the filling to cool for 10 minutes before serving.

•

# Kiwi and Cheese Tortillas

**Serves: 4**

**Nutritional value per serving**

| Calories: 211 | Fat: 6g | Carbohydrate: 36g |
| --- | --- | --- |
| Protein: 5g | Dietary Fibre: 4g | |

## Ingredients

- 4 tbs low-fat cream cheese
- 4 flour tortillas
- 4 tsp low sugar strawberry jam
- 4 kiwi fruit, peeled and thinly sliced

Spread the cream cheese equally over the tortillas, and then spread the strawberry jam over half of each tortilla. Place the kiwi slices over the other half of each tortilla. Fold the two sides together and serve.

•

# Chicken Tortillas

**Serves: 6**

**Nutritional value per serving**

| Calories: 120 | Fat: 2g | Carbohydrate: 15g |
| --- | --- | --- |
| Protein: 11g | Dietary Fibre: 1g | |

## Ingredients

- 6 low-fat flour tortillas
- 3 chicken breasts, cooked and shredded
- 225g low-fat cream cheese, softened
- 6 spring onions, thinly sliced
- 2 tbs low-fat sour cream
- 1 bunch fresh dill, chopped
- 6 fresh lettuce leaves, roughly chopped

Combine the shredded chicken with the cream cheese, onions, sour cream and dill in a mixing bowl; mix until blended. Spread the mixture evenly on the tortillas, add the chopped lettuce and then roll tightly.

Wrap each tortilla in a food standard plastic bag and refrigerate for at least 1 hour before serving.

•

## Avocado and Mango Tortillas

**Serves: 4**

**Nutritional value per serving**

Calories: 169 Fat: 8g Carbohydrate: 26g

Protein: 2g Dietary Fibre: 5g

### Ingredients

1 large avocado, stoned and mashed
1 large mango, peeled and cut into 2cm cubes
3 tbs fresh lime juice
2 tsp sweetener
½ tsp minced jalapeno pepper
100g baked corn tortilla chips

Combine the lime juice, sugar and jalapeno pepper in a mixing bowl; mix half with the avocado and marinate the mango with the remainder.

When serving, place 2 cubes of mango on a tortilla chip and cover with a teaspoon of mashed avocado.

•

## Cuban Meatball Tortillas

**Serves: 6**

**Nutritional value per serving**

Calories: 340 Fat: 19g Carbohydrate: 28g

Protein: 19g Dietary Fibre: 4g

### Salsa

1 cup mild or medium chunky salsa
2 tbs coarsely chopped herbs

### Meatballs

450g lean ground beef
200g rolled oats
1 red onion, finely chopped
50ml skimmed milk
1 clove garlic, minced
1½ tbs fresh mixed herbs, coarsely chopped

| |
|---|
| 1 tsp dried oregano |
| ½ tsp ground cumin |
| 6 flour tortillas, warmed |

Combine all the salsa ingredients in a mixing bowl; mix well and then set aside.

Form the meatballs by combining all the meatball ingredients in large bowl, mix lightly but thoroughly.

Shape into 18 meatballs; place on a greased ovenproof dish and cook in a preheated oven at 180°C for 30 minutes.

Serve the meatballs with the tortillas and a spoonful of salsa on the side.

•

# Chicken Vegetable Soup

**Serves: 4**

**Nutritional value per serving**

Calories: 260 | Fat: 4.1g | Carbohydrate: 29.9g

Protein: 24g | Dietary Fibre: 0.6g

## Ingredients

| |
|---|
| 4 chicken breasts, boned, skinned and cut into 2cm pieces |
| 1 tbs olive oil |
| 1 large onion, coarsely chopped |
| 2 medium carrots, sliced |
| 3 cloves garlic, minced |
| ½ tsp dried thyme |
| ½ tsp dried oregano |
| 4 cups chicken stock |
| salt and pepper to season |

Heat the oil in a large soup saucepan. Sauté the garlic and onions until translucent; add the chicken pieces and continue cooking until the chicken is golden brown on all sides.

Add the stock, carrots, garlic and herbs to saucepan; heat to boiling and then simmer, uncovered, for 20 minutes.

Season to taste.

•

# African Squash Soup

**Serves: 6**

**Nutritional value per serving**

Calories: 111 | Fat: Negligible | Carbohydrate: 20g
Protein: 7g | Dietary Fibre: 3g

## Ingredients

- 1 onion, chopped
- ½ cup apple purée
- 1 tsp mild curry powder
- 1 tsp ground cumin
- ½ tsp ground cinnamon
- ½ tsp ground ginger
- ¼ tsp ground cardamom
- ¼ tsp freshly ground black pepper
- 1 whole squash, skinned and coarsely chopped
- 700ml fat-free chicken stock
- 600ml evaporated skimmed milk

Sauté the onion in a soup saucepan over medium heat until translucent. When ready, add a little of the chicken stock, the apple purée and herbs. Bring to a boil, then reduce the heat.

Add the squash, remaining chicken stock and bring to a boil. Reduce the heat and cook, covered, for 20 minutes. Remove from the heat and stir in the milk. Pour the mixture into a food processor and purée until a smooth texture is formed.

•

# African Vegetable Soup

**Serves: 4**

**Nutritional value per serving**

Calories: 402 | Fat: 3g | Carbohydrate: 75g
Protein: 25g | Dietary Fibre: 27g

## Ingredients

- 2 onions
- 2 red peppers, coarsely chopped
- 100g button mushrooms, sliced
- 2 tbs olive oil
- 2 tsp hot curry powder

- 1 tbs grated coconut
- 250g cooked kidney beans
- 2 cups hot water
- 1 x 340g tin chopped tomatoes
- 4 tbs tomato purée
- 6 large broccoli florets

Heat the oil in a large saucepan. When hot, sauté the onions, peppers and mushrooms, stir in the curry powder and grated coconut; then set aside in a bowl and keep warm. Pour the hot water into a saucepan, turn up the heat and allow the water to boil. Now add the kidney beans, tomatoes, tomato purée and broccoli florets. Simmer for about 20 minutes and then add the curried vegetables. Continue cooking for a further 5 minutes. Serve hot.

•

## Wild Rice Chicken Soup

**Serves: 4**

**Nutritional value per serving**

Calories: 250 Fat: 3.8g Carbohydrate: 24.6g
Protein: 29g Dietary Fibre: 1g

### Ingredients

- 450g chicken breast, cut into 1cm cubes
- 1 tsp olive oil
- 1 onion, roughly chopped
- 500ml reduced-sodium chicken stock
- ½ cup wild rice
- 2 carrots, thinly sliced
- 1 small head broccoli, cut into florets
- 1 tsp dried sage
- salt and pepper for seasoning

Heat the chicken in hot olive oil in a large saucepan until lightly browned. Add the onion and cook until tender. Stir in the chicken stock, wild rice and carrots. Heat to boiling and then reduce the heat and simmer, covered, for 45 minutes, or until the rice is tender.

Stir in the broccoli and sage; simmer until the broccoli is tender. Season to taste with salt and pepper.

•

# Boston Rice Soup

**Serves: 2**

**Nutritional value per serving**

Calories: 64 Fat: 1.3g Carbohydrate: 4.9g

Protein: 7.3g Dietary Fibre: 0g

## Ingredients

- 4 cups chicken stock
- 25g long-grain rice
- 3 cloves garlic, minced
- juice of 1 fresh lime
- 1 egg, lightly beaten
- 2 tbs fresh parsley, finely chopped
- low-salt bouillon powder for seasoning

Heat the stock to boiling in a soup saucepan; stir in the rice and garlic. Reduce the heat and simmer, covered for 25 minutes, or until the rice is tender.

Keeping the soup over a low heat, whisk together the lime juice and egg, and slowly stir the mixture into the soup. Stir in the parsley; season to taste with bouillon powder. Serve hot.

•

# French Meatball Soup

**Serves 1**

**Nutritional value per serving**

Calories: 71 Fat: 6.7g Carbohydrate:

Protein: 15g Dietary Fibre: 15.5g

## Ingredients

- 2 tbs cooked basmati rice
- 50g ground beef
- 1 small onion, finely chopped
- 2 cloves garlic, finely chopped
- sprinkling of fresh parsley
- sprinkling of nutmeg
- 2 tbs dry red wine

| 200ml beef stock |
|---|

Mix together the rice, beef, onion, garlic, parsley and nutmeg, and form into small meatballs.

Using a stainless steel saucepan, heat the wine and stock until boiling. Add the meatballs to the stock, one at a time, bring back to the boil, and then simmer for 20 minutes.

Add salt and pepper.

•

# Cannellini Bean Soup

**Serves: 4**

**Nutritional value per serving**

Calories: 293 Fat: 11g Carbohydrate: 15g

Protein: 13g Dietary Fibre: 6g

## Ingredients

| 1 onion, chopped |
|---|
| 2 cloves garlic, crushed |
| 1 tbs olive oil |
| 225g tinned cannellini beans, drained and rinsed |
| 2 litres fresh water |
| 2 bay leaves, large |
| 1 tsp dried basil, chopped |
| ½ tsp salt |
| ½ tsp white pepper, ground |
| 2 tbs parsley, fresh chopped |
| 2 spring onion, chopped |

Heat 2 tablespoons of olive oil in a large stainless steel saucepan, add the onion and garlic, and sauté until translucent, stirring often.

Add the beans, water, bay leaves and basil. When the water begins to boil, reduce to a simmer and cover. Continue cooking until the beans are tender, adding more liquid if necessary and stirring occasionally. Season with salt and pepper. When cooked, turn off the heat and leave the ingredients in the saucepan to cool.

Remove the bay leaves from the soup then purée the beans in a blender.

Return the puréed soup to the saucepan and reheat over a moderate flame, stirring often. If the soup is too thick, add water or chicken broth.

Serve hot directly from a turine, garnishing each bowl with chopped parsley and green onions.

•

## Vegetable Soup

**Serves: 8**

**Nutritional value per serving**

Calories: 117 Fat: 1g Carbohydrate: 26g

Protein: 5g Dietary Fibre: 4g

### Ingredients

- 2 medium courgettes, thinly sliced
- 2 carrots, sliced
- 10 button mushrooms, sliced
- 2 ribs celery
- 450g sweetcorn, tinned or frozen
- 1 potato, peeled, cut into 2.5cm chunks
- 225g green beans, cut in half diagonally
- 1 litre vegetable broth
- 1 tin chopped plum tomatoes, drained
- ½ cup chopped fresh parsley
- 4 cloves garlic, crushed
- ¼ cup chopped fresh basil
- ¼ cup chopped fresh oregano
- salt and freshly ground black pepper, to season

Combine all the vegetables and the broth in a large stainless steel saucepan then cook over a medium heat until the broth begins to boil.

Reduce to a simmer and cover. Continue cooking until the ingredients are tender, adding more liquid if necessary. Season to taste, stirring occasionally.

•

## Italian Vegetable Soup

**Serves: 6**

**Nutritional value per serving**

Calories: 216 Fat: 4g Carbohydrate: 11g Protein: 12g Dietary Fibre: 4.4g

Low-sodium diets: Omit salt. Substitute canned vegetables and chicken stock.

## Ingredients

- 150g dry haricot beans
- 1 small courgette, sliced
- 1 celery stalk, sliced
- 4 cups chicken stock
- 100g garbanzo beans
- 2 carrots, sliced
- 1 medium size potato, scrubbed and sliced
- ½ cup Rotini or other pasta
- 1 tbs corn oil
- 1 onion, sliced
- 1 tbs fresh parsley; finely minced
- 450g tin Italian tomatoes
- 2 tbs dried basil, crumbled
- ½ small cabbage; sliced thinly
- salt and ground pepper for seasoning

Cover haricot beans with fresh water in a large cooking pot. Bring just to boiling point over a medium heat. Remove pan from heat, cover and let stand for 1 hour.

Drain off the water and replace with the chicken stock. Add the carrots and potato slices. Cover and cook over medium heat until vegetables are almost tender, about 35 minutes.

Heat the corn oil in a small frying pan and sauté the onion until translucent.

Add onion and all remaining ingredients to the cooking pot. Cook for further 15 minutes, or until the pasta is cooked.

•

# Barley Soup

**Serves: 6**

**Nutritional value per serving**

Calories: 181 | Fat: 2g | Carbohydrate: 30g

Protein: 11g | Dietary Fibre: 2.4g

## Ingredients

- 900ml chicken stock
- 50g pot barley
- 1 onion, chopped
- 2 celery stalks, chopped
- 3 carrots; sliced

1 bay leaf
1 tsp dry thyme
¼ tsp dried marjoram
¼ tsp ground black pepper
2 tbs chopped fresh parsley

Combine all the ingredients in a stainless steel saucepan.

Cook over a low heat for 1 hour, or until the carrots are tender and the barley is soft. Remove the bay leaf before serving.

Basmati long-grain rice has slightly fewer carbohydrates and calories than barley if you wish to substitute.

•

# German Cabbage Soup

**Serves: 1**

**Nutritional value per serving**

Calories: 104    Fat: 7.4g    Carbohydrate: 2.5g
Protein: 11g    Dietary Fibre: 2.1g

## Ingredients

1 cup finely sliced cabbage leaves
50g ground lean beef
1¼ cups beef broth
½ medium size onion, finely sliced
1 tsp German mustard
1 tsp soy sauce
1 tbs dry red wine
½ tsp fresh parsley
1 medium size tomato, chopped
salt and pepper for seasoning

Combine ground beef, onion, mustard, soy sauce, and mix thoroughly. Form into small meatballs. Add the wine to the broth in a stainless steel saucepan then bring to boil over a medium heat. Add the meatballs to the broth, one at a time. Bring to a boil again. Cook for a further 5 minutes then remove the meatballs to a dish and keep hot. Add the cabbage and tomatoes to the broth. Simmer for a further 5 minutes.

To serve, pour the broth over the meatballs. Garnish with parsley.

•

## Lentil Soup

**Serves: 8**

**Nutritional value per serving**

Calories: 92 Fat: 2g Carbohydrate: 23g
Protein: 1g Dietary Fibre: 8g

### Ingredients

- 2 onions, rough chopped
- 4 cloves garlic, crushed
- 80g dried apricots, chopped
- 360g red lentils
- 4 cups chicken stock
- 1 x 340g tin chopped plum tomatoes, juice included
- ½ tsp dried thyme
- salt to taste
- ground black pepper to taste
- 1 large carrot, sliced

Heat the stock to boiling point, then add all the ingredients and reheat until almost boiling; reduce the heat and simmer for 45 minutes.

When the vegetables are tender, taste and add more seasoning if required.

•

## Greek Egg Soup

**Serves: 4**

**Nutritional value per serving**

Calories: 69 Fat: 3g; Carbohydrate: 15.5g
Protein: 4g Dietary Fibre: 0.1g

### Ingredients

- 2 eggs
- ½ tsp mixed herbs
- 4 cups boiling water
- sprinkling ground black pepper
- 2 tbs basmati rice
- 2 eggs, beaten
- sprigs of parsley

2 tbs fresh lemon juice

Bring the water to the boil in a stainless steel saucepan, add the rice to the water and bring back to the boil. Cover and let simmer gently for 15 minutes or until the rice is tender but firm.

Separate the egg whites from the yolks and discard the yolks. Combine the egg whites with the lemon juice and add to the rice, stirring all the time. Turn down the heat and keep stirring until the mixture is smooth.

Season with the black pepper and mixed herbs then serve with a sprig of parsley.

•

## Courgette Soup

**Serves: 4**

**Nutritional value per serving**

Calories: 25 Fat: 4g; Carbohydrate: 0.2g

Protein: 3g; Dietary Fibre: 1.2g

### Ingredients

450g courgettes, cleaned and thinly sliced

1 onion, finely chopped

2 tbs water

½ tsp powdered turmeric

1 tbs margarine

3 cloves garlic, crushed

½ cup skimmed milk

1¾ cups chicken stock

Heat the margarine in a stainless steel saucepan. Add the onion, garlic, courgettes and water. (Set aside a few slices of courgette for garnish.) Cover and simmer gently for 10 minutes, stirring while cooking.

Remove from the heat; add all the remaining ingredients and mix well. Turn into a blender and blend for 30 seconds.

Garnish each bowl with thin slices of courgette before serving.

Courgette soup is delicious served hot or well chilled.

•

# Beef and Barley Soup

**Serves: 8**

**Nutritional value per serving**

Calories: 56 | Fat: 2g | Carbohydrate: 15g

Protein: 8g; | Dietary Fibre: 7.3g

## Ingredients

- 230g stewing beef, cut into 2cm cubes
- ½ cup pot barley, soaked overnight
- 2 large carrots, sliced
- 6 cups fresh water
- 2 leeks sliced
- 2 stalks celery, sliced
- 1 bay leaf
- sprinkling black peppercorns
- 1 onion, finely chopped
- 1 sprig parsley, chopped

Place the meat, water, bay leaf and peppercorns in a large stainless steel saucepan, bring to the boil then cover and simmer for 1 hour, skimming off the foam occasionally.

Add the pot barley, celery, carrots, leeks and onion to the soup and bring back to boil. Reduce heat and simmer for about 30 minutes or until the barley is tender.

Serve garnished with parsley.

•

# Wiltshire Ham with Pasta

**Serves: 4**

**Nutritional value per serving**

Calories: 421 | Fat: 12g | Carbohydrate: 58g

Protein: 22g | Dietary Fibre: 2g

## Ingredients

- 350g pasta twists, cooked
- 75g frozen peas
- 2 tsp olive oil
- 2 cloves garlic, crushed
- 120g Wiltshire ham, chopped
- 250ml low-fat sour cream

| |
|---|
| 40g shredded Parmesan cheese |
| 120ml skimmed milk |
| 1 tbs plain flour |
| 1 tbs chopped fresh basil |

Sauté the garlic in hot oil in a stainless steel saucepan, add the ham, and stir-fry for 1 minute.

Blend the sour cream, Parmesan cheese, milk and flour; stir in the ham mixture; cook and stir until slightly thickened. Reduce heat to low.

Add the pasta and basil; toss to coat.

Cook until thoroughly heated.

•

# Barbecue Pork Kebabs

**Serves: 4**

**Nutritional value per serving**

Calories: 169 Fat: 6g Carbohydrate: 5g

Protein: 22g Dietary Fibre: 0.5g

## Ingredients

| |
|---|
| 3 tbs soy sauce |
| 2 tbs rice wine vinegar |
| 1 tbs lemon juice |
| 1 tsp hot pepper sauce |
| 330g pork tenderloin, cut into 3cm cubes |
| 1 red pepper, cut into 4cm squares |
| 1 small cucumber, cut into 2cm slices |

Mix all the ingredients, except the pork and vegetables, in a bowl; add the pork pieces to the marinade and marinate in a refrigerator for 1 hour.

Remove the pork from the marinade with a slotted spoon. Then thread the cubed pork, peppers and cucumber alternately onto the skewers.

Barbecue the kebabs on each side for 10 minutes, or until cooked right through.

•

# Mexican Pork Cutlets

**Serves: 4**

**Nutritional value per serving**

| | | |
|---|---|---|
| Calories: 258 | Calories | Carbohydrate: 8 g |
| Protein: 27g | Dietary Fibre: 0g | |

## Ingredients

- 2 tbs olive oil
- 1 red onion, finely chopped
- 3 cloves garlic, finely chopped
- plain flour, as required
- 4 pork chops, boned and flattened
- sprinkling ground cumin
- ½ cup chicken stock
- ½ tsp red wine
- 1 cup salsa

Heat the oil in a deep non-stick frying pan over medium-high heat. Add the onion and garlic and sauté, stirring occasionally for 2 minutes or until translucent.

Sprinkle some flour on waxed paper. Lightly coat the chops in flour.

Add the cutlets to the pan; sauté for 2 minutes on each side or until golden brown. Add the cumin, stock, wine and salsa; cook for about 5 minutes, or until the cutlets are cooked through.

•

# Apple Pork Chops

**Serves: 4**

**Nutritional value per serving**

| | | |
|---|---|---|
| Calories: 270 | Fat: 12g | Carbohydrate: 15 g |
| Protein: 20g | Dietary Fibre: Trace | |

## Ingredients

- 4 pork chops
- 2 crisp eating apples, peeled, cored and sliced
- 2 tbs plain flour
- 2 tbs raisins
- 1 tsp ground cinnamon

Coat the pork chops on all sides with the flour then place in a casserole dish.

Arrange the apple slices and raisins around the pork chops and then sprinkle with ground cinnamon. Cover the casserole dish and bake in a preheated oven at 230ºC for 40 minutes.

Remove the covering and spoon the apple mixture over the pork chops. Return to the oven and bake for a further 15-20 minutes, or until the chops are golden and cooked through.

•

# Baked Pork Chops

**Serves: 4**

**Nutritional value per serving**

Calories: 240 Carbohydrates: 3g Fat: 14g

Protein: 25g Dietary Fibre: 0.7g

## Ingredients

- 4 pork chops, boned and trimmed
- 1 tsp dried basil
- 1 tsp black pepper
- 1 cup vegetable stock

Arrange the chops in a casserole dish and cover with the remaining ingredients. Place in a preheated oven at 180ºC, cover and cook for 40 minutes or until tender.

•

# Swedish Meatballs

**Serves: 6**

**Nutritional value per serving**

Calories: 106 Fat: 3g Carbohydrate: 5g

Protein: 15g Dietary Fibre: 0g

## Ingredients

- 1 small egg
- 2 tbs skimmed milk
- 30g breadcrumbs
- 1 shallot, finely chopped
- 1 tsp dried parsley
- ¼ tsp mixed spice
- ¼ tsp nutmeg

| |
|---|
| 225g lamb, finely minced |
| 120g pork sausage meat |
| 1½ tbs plain flour |
| 2 tsp olive oil |

Whisk the egg, milk and breadcrumbs in a large bowl then let it stand for 5 minutes for the breadcrumbs to soak up the egg and milk. Add the shallot, parsley, mixed spice and nutmeg; blend well. Add the lamb and pork sausage meat and stir with a fork until well mixed. Cover and chill for at least 30 minutes.

•

# Stir-fry Pork Medley

**Serves: 6**

**Nutritional value per serving**

Calories: 172 Fat: 6g Carbohydrate: 8g

Protein: 21g Dietary Fibre: 2g

## Ingredients

| |
|---|
| 1 tbs soy sauce |
| 1 tbs cornflour |
| 1 tsp chilli powder |
| ½ cup cold fresh water |
| 450g pork sirloin, cut into strips |
| 1 tbs olive oil |
| 3 clove garlic, crushed |
| 1 small piece fresh ginger, finely sliced |
| 2 stalks celery, sliced |
| 3 carrots, sliced |
| 6 florets broccoli, chopped in halves |
| 6 small button mushrooms, sliced |
| 1 red pepper, coarsely chopped |
| 4 spring onions, thinly sliced |

Stir the soy sauce, cornflour and chilli powder into the water to make a sauce, and then set aside.

Heat the olive oil in a wok over high heat. Add the sliced pork, garlic and ginger; stir-fry until the meat is lightly browned. Add the vegetables to the wok and stir-fry for a further 3 minutes.

Drizzle the sauce into the wok; cover and cook for 5 minutes, or until the vegetables are tender.

Flour a pastry board and shape the meat into 24 meatballs, about 1 tablespoon each. Coat each meatball lightly in the flour and set aside.

Heat the olive oil in a heavy gauge non-stick frying pan. Add the meatballs and cook for 20-25 minutes, turning occasionally until browned on all sides.

•

# French Lamb Stew

**Serves: 4**

**Nutritional value per serving**

Calories: 287 Fat: 9g Carbohydrates: 21g

Protein: 30g Dietary Fibre: 3g

## Ingredients

450g stewing lamb, cut into 2cm chunks
1 tbs olive oil
1 large potato, diced
2 carrots, sliced
3 cloves garlic, crushed
1 tsp cinnamon
½ tsp ground coriander
¼ tsp ground cinnamon
¼ tsp black pepper
1 tsp corn flour
225ml chicken stock
2 tbs chopped parsley

Mix the cinnamon, coriander and pepper in a bowl; add the lamb chunks and coat with the spices.

Heat the oil in a large stewing pan; add the lamb pieces and brown on all sides. Add the carrots, potato and garlic and sauté for 5 minutes.

Stir the cornflour into the stock; then add the stock to the stewing pan and bring to a boil. Lower the heat and simmer for 20-25 minutes, or until the lamb is tender and vegetables are cooked though. Garnish with chopped parsley before serving.

•

# Chilli Beef

**Serves: 4**

**Nutritional value per serving**

Calories: 252 Fat: 8g Carbohydrate: 17g
Protein: 31g Dietary Fibre: 4g

## Ingredients

- 450g beef sirloin, coarsely ground
- 1 tbs olive oil
- 1 onion, chopped
- 3 cloves garlic, crushed
- 1 red pepper, deseeded and chopped
- 1 tsp chilli powder
- 1 tsp ground cumin
- 1 tsp dried oregano
- 1 x 435g tin chopped tomatoes
- 120ml beef stock

## Topping

- 1 x 150g carton of plain non-fat yoghurt
- 2 tbs fresh coriander, finely chopped
- 1 tsp chilli powder
- pinch of cayenne pepper

Sauté the onions and garlic in hot olive oil until translucent. Add the ground beef and continue cooking until the beef has changed colour. Drain off any fat or juices.

Add the remaining ingredients to the beef; increase the heat and allow the stock to bubble, then turn down the heat and simmer for 30-35 minutes, or until the beef is thoroughly cooked.

Combine all the topping ingredients in a bowl and mix thoroughly. Place the topping on the table for individuals to help themselves.

•

# Beef and Tomato Bouillon

**Serves: 6**

**Nutritional value per serving**

Calories: 38 Fat: 0g Carbohydrate: 7g
Protein: 3g Dietary Fibre: 1g

### Ingredients

- 4 cups fresh tomato juice
- 1 small tin low-salt beef soup
- 1 tsp light soy sauce
- 1 tsp Worcestershire sauce
- 1 tbs chopped parsley

Combine all the ingredients except the parsley in a stainless steel saucepan. Simmer until hot. Serve hot, garnished with chopped parsley.

•

## German Stew

**Serves: 4**

**Nutritional value per serving**

| Calories: 178 | Fat: 5g | Carbohydrate: 20g |
| --- | --- | --- |
| Protein: 13g | Dietary Fibre: 1g | |

### Ingredients

- 225g extra lean minced beef
- 2 tbs olive oil
- 1 onion, coarsely chopped
- 1 cup basmati rice, cooked
- 2 cups sauerkraut, drained
- 3 tomatoes, skinned
- 1 tsp sweetener
- 1 tsp dried parsley

Heat the oil in a large saucepan and brown the minced beef; add the chopped onion and cook until the onions are translucent.

Add the rice, sauerkraut, tomatoes and sweetener. Turn up the heat until the mixture begins to bubble, and then lower the heat and simmer for 15 minutes. Sprinkle the parsley into the stew, stirring occasionally for another 3 minutes.

•

# Portuguese Beef Stew

**Serves: 6**

**Nutritional value per serving**

Calories: 156 Fat: 8g Carbohydrate: 8g
Protein: 18g Dietary Fibre: 0g

## Ingredients

| |
|---|
| 450g loin beef, sliced |
| 2 tsp olive oil |
| 3 onions, thinly sliced |
| 2 garlic cloves, crushed |
| 1 x 400g tin chopped tomatoes |
| 1 tsp fresh parsley, chopped |
| 1 bay leaf |
| pinch salt |
| pepper to taste |
| 1 tbs fresh herbs, chopped |

Heat the olive oil over medium high heat and brown the beef slices for 2 minutes.
Add the onion, garlic, tomatoes, parsley and bay leaf. Season to taste with salt and pepper.
Bring the liquid up to boiling point and then simmer, covered for 30 minutes.
Adding a teaspoon of cornflour mixed in a little cold water may reduce the liquid down. Alternatively, removing the lid will allow it to evaporate.
Garnish with fresh herbs of your choice before serving.

•

# Beef Stew

**Serves 4**

**Nutritional value per serving**

Calories: 326 Fat: 5.8g Carbohydrates: 29.6g
Protein: 33.5g Dietary Fibre: 0g

## Ingredients

| |
|---|
| 450g lean stewing beef, fat trimmed, cubed |
| 1 tbs olive oil |
| 1 large shallot, chopped |
| 1 stick of celery, chopped |

- 2 cloves garlic, finely sliced
- 1 vegetable stock cube
- 1 cup beef stock
- 1 tbs tomato paste
- 1 sprig of thyme, chopped
- 1 sprig of rosemary, chopped
- 1 bay leaf
- 2 large potatoes, cubed
- 2 large carrots, sliced
- 1 thick slice of turnip, peeled and cubed
- 2 tbs plain flour
- ¼ cup cold water
- fresh milled black pepper for seasoning

Heat the oil in a large stainless steel saucepan; add the beef and brown on all sides to seal in the juices. Add the onion, celery and garlic; cook until tender. Add the beef stock, tomato paste and herbs; heat to boiling then reduce the heat and simmer, covered for 1½ hours, or until the beef is tender. Add remaining vegetables during last 30 minutes of cooking time.

Mix the flour and water; bring the stew to boiling. Then stir the flour mixture into the stew. Keep the stew on the boil, stirring constantly, until the juices have thickened. Discard the bay leaf and season to taste.

•

## Veal Burgers

**Serves: 4**

**Nutritional value per serving**

Calories: 172 | Fat: 6g | Carbohydrates: 14g

Protein: 16g | Dietary Fibre: 2g

### Ingredients

- 350g ground veal
- 1 onion, finely chopped
- 2 cloves garlic, crushed
- 1 egg, whipped
- 4 tbs breadcrumbs
- 1 tbs tomato paste
- 1 tbs dried sage

- 1 tbs garlic powder
- 1 tbs low salt soy sauce
- 1 cup boiling water
- plain flour as required

Place the breadcrumbs and sage in a mixing bowl with a cup of boiling water and allow the mixture to soak up all the liquid.

Combine all the ingredients in a mixing bowl; then flatten into 8 burgers on a floured board. Place on a baking sheet and bake in a preheated oven at 200°C for approximately ten minutes or until no longer pink inside. Place in a serving dish and serve with vegetables of your choice.

•

## Beef Teriyaki

**Servings: 5**

**Nutritional value per serving**

Calories: 100 Fat: 3g Carbohydrate: 1g

Protein: 17g Dietary Fibre: 0g

### Ingredients

- 450g boneless sirloin steak, cut into 2cm cubes
- ¼ cup soy sauce
- ¼ cup chicken stock
- 1 tbs olive oil
- ½ tsp ground ginger
- 1 tsp sweetener
- 1 clove garlic, chopped

Place the beef in a mixing bowl. Add the remaining ingredients; cover and marinate in a refrigerator for at least 1 hour, stirring occasionally.

Take 5 wooden skewers; divide the beef cubes into 5 portions and skewer the cubes.

Place the skewered meat in a shallow broiling dish and pour the marinade over the top. Cook in a preheated oven at 200°C until the meat is cooked right through. Brush with the remaining marinade before serving.

•

# Barbecued Steak Kebabs

**Serves: 4**

**Nutritional value per serving**

Calories: 194 Fat: 7g Carbohydrate: 9g
Protein: 23g Dietary Fibre: 2g

## Ingredients

450g sirloin steak, trimmed of any fat, cut into 2cm cubes
1 tbs olive oil
1 large green pepper, deseeded and cut into 2cm squares
1 large red pepper, deseeded and cut into 2cm squares
3 tomatoes, thickly sliced

## Sauce

¼ cup low salt soy sauce
1 tbs honey
2 tbs dry sherry
1 tsp orange zest

Combine the soy sauce, honey, sherry, zest and oil in a large plastic or glass dish. Add the cubed beef; cover and marinate in a refrigerator for 2 hours.

Drain the marinade. Soak the wooden skewers in a pan of warm water for 30 minutes and then thread the cubed steak, peppers and tomatoes alternately onto the skewers.

Barbecue the kebabs on each side for 10 minutes, or until cooked right through.

•

# Veal Stew

**Serves: 4**

**Nutritional value per serving**

Calories: 270 Fat: 10g Carbohydrate: 12g
Protein: 29g Dietary Fibre: 2g

## Ingredients

600g veal shoulder, boned and cut into 2cm cubes
3 tbs plain flour
½ tsp dried thyme
¼ tsp crushed dried rosemary
freshly ground pepper

- 1 tbs olive oil
- 100ml dry red wine
- 1 onion, coarsely chopped
- 1 stick celery, sliced
- 1 carrot, diced
- 265g chopped tinned tomatoes
- 415ml chicken stock
- ½ tbs Worcestershire sauce
- 1 bay leaf

Combine the flour, thyme, rosemary and pepper, and lightly coat the veal pieces. Brown the veal pieces in hot oil, turning once. Remove and set aside.

Add the remaining ingredients, bring to the boil and stir in the browned veal.

Simmer, uncovered, for 45 to 55 minutes, or until the veal is tender and the juices have thickened. Remove and discard the bay leaf.

•

## Goulash

**Serves: 6**

**Nutritional value per serving**

Calories: 174 Fat: 2.8g

Protein: 17.6g

### Ingredients

- 450g ground lean beef
- 1 tbs olive oil
- 2 medium onions, chopped
- 1 green pepper, chopped
- 1 red pepper, chopped
- 2 cloves garlic, minced
- 1 tbs flour
- 2 tsp paprika
- 1 cup beef stock
- 1 jar sauerkraut, drained
- 1 large tomato, coarsely chopped
- 1 cup fat-free sour cream
- salt and pepper, to taste
- Minced parsley, for garnishing

Heat the olive oil in a large non-stick saucepan. When hot, add the onions and garlic; sauté until translucent.

Add the ground beef and cook until the meat is browned. Add the peppers and continue cooking until the peppers have softened.

Stir in the flour and paprika; cook for a further 1 to 2 minutes.

Stir in the sauerkraut, tomato and sour cream; add the beef stock, then season to taste with salt and pepper.

Whilst still hot, pour the prepared ingredients into a casserole dish; cover and bake in a preheated oven at 180°C for 20 to 30 minutes. Sprinkle with parsley before serving.

•

# Oven-Baked Italian Omelette

**Serves: 6**

**Nutrition Information Per Serving**

| Calories: 152 | Fat: 6g | Carbohydrates: 15g |
|---|---|---|
| Protein: 11g | Dietary Fibre: 3g | |

## Ingredients

| |
|---|
| 1½ cups liquid egg substitute |
| olive oil, as required |
| 1 Charlotte potato, peeled and thinly sliced |
| 1 onion, thinly sliced |
| 3 cloves garlic, crushed |
| freshly milled black pepper |
| 125g button mushrooms, thinly sliced |
| 1 small aubergine, peeled and thinly sliced |
| 2 tomatoes, thinly sliced |
| ½ tsp Italian herb seasoning |
| ¼ cup grated Parmesan cheese |

Arrange the potato and onion slices in a baking tin, sprinkle with crushed garlic and brush with olive oil. Bake in a preheated oven at 230°C, uncovered, for 15 minutes.

Add the mushroom and aubergine slices and brush with olive oil. Continue to bake for a further 10 minutes.

Add the tomato slices, herbs and cheese. Pour the egg substitute over the vegetables and, using a knife, slightly move the layers of vegetables to allow the egg substitute to flow to the bottom.

Bake, uncovered, for about 20 minutes, until the omelette is puffed and golden brown, and a knife inserted into the centre comes out clean.

•

## Stuffed Spanish Onions

**Serves: 4**

### Nutrition Information Per Serving

Calories: 449 | Fat: 19g | Carbohydrates: 36g
Protein: 36g | Dietary Fibre: 3g

### Ingredients

4 Spanish onions
350g minced turkey breast
1 tbs olive oil
2 large cloves garlic, crushed
2 large plum tomatoes, deseeded and finely chopped
2 tbs tomato paste
2 tsp mixed herbs
freshly ground pepper, to taste
1 egg white
2 cups chicken stock

Cut a slice from the root end and top quarter of each onion. Cut a cone shape into each onion and, using a small spoon, scoop out the centre, leaving a shell about 1cm thick.

Finely chop the onion centres and set aside. Cook the onion shells in boiling water until the shells are tender but still hold their shape. Using a slotted spoon, remove the onion shells from the water and drain upside down on paper towels.

Sauté the onion centres and garlic in hot oil until translucent. Add the turkey and sauté until no longer pink. Stir in the tomatoes, tomato paste and mixed herbs.

Spoon the turkey mixture into the onion shells, mounding slightly on top.

Place the stuffed onions in a baking tin; pour the chicken stock over the onions and cook in a preheated oven at 160°C for 1 hour.

•

# Braised Whole Artichokes

### Serves: 4

**Nutrition Information Per Serving**

Calories: 80 Fat: 2.4g Carbohydrates: 13.4g

Protein: 4.2g Dietary Fibre: ½g

## Ingredients

- 1 lemon
- 3 artichokes
- ½ teaspoon salt
- red oak leaf lettuce leaves, prepared
- 1 tbs balsamic vinegar
- 50ml olive oil
- salt and ground black pepper for seasoning

Prepare the artichokes first. Break off the stems removing the tough fibres from the centre of the base. Cut off the tough bottom leaves from the artichokes. Clip off the spiny tops of the other leaves. Carefully spread the leaves apart until you can see the inner central cone. Pull out the cone in one piece and scoop out the hairy fibres with a spoon.

Slice the lemon in half. With one half of the lemon, rub the juice into the sliced leaves to prevent them being discoloured. Squeeze the other half of the lemon into a bowl of cold water and plunge the artichokes into the water.

Add the salt and some of the lemon juice to a pan of water (do not use an aluminium or iron pan). Gently braise the artichokes, uncovered for 30 to 40 minutes. The leaves will easily pull off when cooked.

Place the lettuce leaves on a serving dish and season with salt and pepper. Chop the artichokes and place on top of the lettuce. Drizzle the olive oil and balsamic vinegar over the top.

•

# Castilian Hash

### Serves: 6

**Nutritional value per serving**

Calories: 191 Fat: 7g Carbohydrates: 16g

Protein: 16g Dietary Fibre: 2g

### Ingredients

- 450g ground beef
- 250ml water
- 1 beef stock cube
- 2 shallots, finely chopped
- 2 potatoes, diced
- 2 tbs tomato sauce
- 1 tbs chopped almonds
- 75g seedless raisins
- 25g brown sugar
- 3 cloves garlic, thinly sliced
- 1 tsp dried parsley

Crush 1 beef stock cube into 250ml boiling water and pour into a saucepan. Add the beef to the saucepan and cook over a medium heat for 10 minutes or until meat is browned, stirring occasionally.

Add the shallots, potatoes and tomato sauce. Mix well to combine. Stir in the almonds, raisins, brown sugar, garlic and parsley. Continue cooking for 10 minutes, or until the potatoes are tender, stirring often.

•

## Garlic Spinach

**Serves: 4**

**Nutrition Information Per Serving**

Calories: 110 Fat: 2g Carbohydrates: 16g
Protein: 13g Dietary Fibre: 12g

### Ingredients

- 700g fresh spinach
- 1 teaspoon olive oil
- 2 cloves garlic, thinly sliced

Sauté the garlic in hot oil for 1 minute; add the spinach and cook for a further minute or two.

Delicious when used as a side dish for Oven-Baked Italian Omelette.

•

## Chicken Breasts with Spinach Filling

**Serves: 4**

**Nutritional value per serving**

Calories: 190 Fat: 5g Carbohydrate: 11g
Protein: 28g Dietary Fibre: 2g

### Ingredients

- 4 large button mushrooms, chopped
- 1 small onion, finely chopped
- 125g frozen chopped spinach, thawed
- 50g shredded low-fat mozzarella cheese, divided
- 25g grated Parmesan cheese
- 4 chicken breasts
- 1 tsp bouillon seasoning
- black pepper for seasoning

Sauté the mushrooms and onion in a pan over a medium-low heat until the onion is tender; remove from the heat; add the spinach, half the mozzarella cheese and all of the Parmesan cheese; mix well and set aside.

Slice the chicken breasts lengthwise down the centre to make a pocket and place in a greased 18 x 24cm roasting tin. Fill the pockets with the spinach mixture. Seal the edges with skewers to completely enclose the spinach filling. Bake in a preheated oven at 180°C for 30-35 minutes. When cooked, remove from the oven; sprinkle with the remaining mozzarella cheese; then return to the oven for 4 minutes to allow the cheese to melt.

•

## Mediterranean Chicken Stew

**Serves: 4**

**Nutritional value per serving**

Calories: 429 Fat: 5g Carbohydrate: 58g
Protein: 39g Dietary Fibre: 8g

### Ingredients

- 1 tbs olive oil
- 2 chicken breasts, skinned and cut into halves
- 2 onions, sliced
- 2 cloves garlic, crushed
- 1 red pepper, deseeded and chopped

| |
|---|
| 1 tsp turmeric |
| ½ tsp ground cinnamon |
| ½ tsp ground ginger |
| 960g sweet potatoes, peeled and cut into cubes |
| 1 x 435g tin chopped tomatoes, drained |
| 30g seedless raisins |
| 2 cups chicken stock |

Heat the oil in a large pan; add the chicken and brown all over; add the onion and cook until translucent. Add all the remaining ingredients; allow the juices to boil, and then reduce the heat and simmer for 1 hour, or until the chicken is cooked right through. If at the end of cooking the juices are too thin, add a little cornflour mixed with cold water and stir into the dish.

•

# Cantonese Stir-fry Chicken

**Serves: 4**

**Nutritional value per serving**

Calories: 265 Fat: 9g Carbohydrate: 13g
Protein: 30g Dietary Fibre: 0.5g

## Ingredients

| |
|---|
| 500g boneless chicken thighs, skinned |
| 2 tbs cornflour |
| 1 tbs olive oil |
| 3 cloves garlic, crushed |
| 100g button mushrooms, sliced |
| 3 stalks celery, sliced diagonally |
| 6 spring onions, sliced |
| 2 salad tomatoes, cut into chunks |
| 8 water chestnuts, sliced |
| 3 tbs low-sodium soy sauce |
| ½ tsp ground ginger |
| ½ tsp red pepper |

Slice the chicken meat into 3cm cubes and coat with the cornflour.

Heat the oil over high heat in a wok. Add the chicken and stir-fry until lightly browned on all sides.

Reduce the heat and add the garlic, mushrooms and celery; stir-fry until the vegetables have softened.

Add the tomatoes and water chestnuts. Season with the ginger and red pepper; stir in the soy sauce; cover and simmer for 5 minutes.

Serve hot on a bed of rice.

•

# Grilled Chicken Breasts with Fruit Salsa

**Serves: 4**

**Nutritional value per serving**

| Calories: 305 | Fat: 6g | Carbohydrate: 30g |
| --- | --- | --- |
| Protein: 32g | Dietary Fibre: 3g | |

## Ingredients

4 skinned and boneless chicken breasts
1 tbs olive oil
freshly milled black pepper

## Salsa

1 x 340g tin crushed pineapple, packed in juice, drained
1 mango, peeled and cubed
½ papaya, peeled and cubed
2 tbs white wine vinegar
1 tbs finely chopped coriander

## Topping

white seedless grapes, sliced in half – as required

Combine all the salsa ingredients in a fruit bowl, cover and refrigerate for 1 hour. Brush the chicken breasts with the olive oil; season with pepper and place under a hot grill for 7 minutes per side, or until no pink remains. To serve: place the fruit salsa on a plate using a few spoonfuls per person. Top with a cooked chicken breast. Garnish with sliced grapes.

•

# Spicy Chicken with Tomatoes

**Serves: 4**

**Nutritional value per serving**

Calories: 225 Fat: 6g Carbohydrate: 28g

Protein: 25g Dietary Fibre: 4g

## Ingredients

- 450g minced chicken breast
- 2 tsp olive oil
- 1 cup brown rice, cooked
- 1 onion, finely chopped
- 2 cloves garlic, finely chopped
- 1 x 400g tin chopped tomatoes
- 1 tbs tomato sauce
- 1 tsp hot red pepper sauce
- ½ tsp dried oregano
- ½ tsp black pepper

Cook the minced chicken breast, onion and garlic in hot oil over a medium heat until the mince has changed colour.

Stir in the tomato sauce, hot pepper sauce, oregano, black pepper and the whole tin of tomatoes with the juice. Bring to a boil, then reduce the heat and simmer uncovered for about 45 minutes.

Stir in the cooked brown rice, simmer for an additional 5 minutes and serve immediately.

•

# Continental Chicken and Prawns with Rice

**Serves: 6**

**Nutritional value per serving**

Calories: 255 Fat: 4g Carbohydrates: 28g

Protein: 26g Dietary Fibre: 4g

## Ingredients

- 300g cooked long grain rice
- 140g chopped cooked chicken
- 450g prawns, peeled
- 120g crabmeat
- 1.5 litres chicken stock

- 1 x 435g tin chopped tomatoes
- 1 onion, finely minced
- 3 cloves garlic, crushed
- 1 stick celery, sliced
- 1 small bunch parsley, chopped
- 2 bay leaves
- 1 tsp dried oregano
- 1 tsp dried thyme
- 1 tsp Worcestershire sauce
- ½ tsp red pepper
- 450g fresh okra, tops and stems removed, cut into rings

Heat the chicken stock, tomatoes, onion, garlic, celery, parsley, bay leaves, oregano and thyme in a large saucepan. Bring to a boil; reduce heat and simmer for 10 minutes. Add the prawns, crabmeat, cooked chicken, Worcestershire sauce and red pepper.

Continue to simmer for another 10 minutes. Add the okra and cook for a further 5 minutes, or until the okra is tender. Remove and discard the bay leaves.

To serve, ladle into soup bowls with a tablespoon of cooked rice on top of each serving.

•

## Chicken in Orange Sauce

**Serves 2**

### Nutritional value per serving

Calories: 311 | Fat: 5.3g | Carbohydrates: 42.8g

Protein: 22.4g | Dietary Fibre: 1.3g

### Ingredients

- 150g chicken breast, skinned, boned and cut into strips
- 20ml fresh orange juice
- 2 tsp cornflour
- 1 tbs olive oil
- 15g chopped cashew nuts
- 225g water chestnuts, drained and sliced
- 50g green capsicum, sliced
- 5 large spring onions, chopped
- 25g grated fresh ginger root

- 75ml fat free chicken broth
- 2 tsp low-sodium soy sauce
- 1 small tin mandarin oranges in light syrup, drained
- 225g brown rice (cooked without salt)

Combine the chicken strips, orange juice and 1 teaspoon of cornflour in a medium size bowl; cover and chill for 1 hour.

Heat the oil in a non-stick pan over a medium heat. Add the cashew nuts; cook, stirring constantly for about 30 seconds until browned. Remove from the pan and set aside on kitchen paper to drain off the oil.

Add the chicken to the pan. Cook uncovered over medium-high heat until the chicken is lightly browned on all sides. Add the water chestnuts, capsicum, spring onions and grated ginger, stir-fry for a further 5 minutes.

Combine the broth, soy sauce and 1 tablespoon cornflour; add to the chicken mixture and bring to a boil; reduce the heat and cook, stirring constantly, until the juices have thickened. Remove from the heat and stir in the oranges. When ready to serve, spoon the chicken and orange sauce over the rice and sprinkle with the cashew nuts.

•

## Baked Cajun Chicken

**Serves: 4**

**Nutritional value per serving**

Calories: 166 Fat: 6g Carbohydrate: 0g
Protein: 25g Dietary Fibre: 0g

### Ingredients

- 700g chicken breasts, boned and skinned
- ½ tsp dried thyme
- non-stick spray coating
- 2 tbs skimmed milk
- 2 tbs onion powder
- ¼ tsp crushed red pepper
- ¼ tsp ground black pepper
- ¼ tsp ground white pepper
- ¼ tsp garlic powder

Spray an ovenproof baking dish with non-stick cooking oil, and then arrange the chicken in the dish brushed lightly with milk.

Combine all the dry ingredients in a small bowl, mix well and then sprinkle over the chicken.

Bake the chicken breasts in a preheated oven at 190°C for 45 minutes, or until brown and tender.

•

# Coq Au Vin

**Serves: 6**

**Nutritional value per serving**

| | | |
|---|---|---|
| Calories: 345 | Fat: 5g | Carbohydrates: 39.5 g |
| Protein: 31.5g | Dietary Fibre: Trace | |

## Ingredients

- 6 chicken breasts boned and skinned
- 2 tbs olive oil
- 3 cloves garlic, thinly sliced
- 4 spring onions, sliced
- 5 pearl onions, peeled, halved
- 250g small button mushrooms
- 8 new potatoes, halved
- ½ tsp dried thyme
- sprinkling of black pepper
- ½ cup water
- ½ cup dry red wine

Heat the oil over a medium heat in a large frying pan. Sauté the garlic and onion until translucent, and then add the chicken breasts. Cook until brown on all sides. Place the contents of the pan in an oven dish. Sprinkle the spring onions, pearl onions, mushrooms and potatoes around the chicken breasts. Finally, add the water and wine to the dish and sprinkle the garlic, thyme and pepper over the chicken breasts. Roast, covered, in a preheated oven at 160°C for 1½ hours, or until tender.

•

# Caribbean Chicken

**Servings: 6**

**Nutritional value per serving**

Calories: 160 | Fat: 6g | Carbohydrate: 6g
Protein: 19g | Dietary Fibre: 0.1g

## Ingredients

- 6 chicken breasts skinned, boned and thinly sliced
- 2 tsp olive oil
- 1 onion, sliced
- 3 cloves garlic, crushed
- 1 tbs apricot chutney
- ½ tsp thyme
- ½ tsp curry powder
- ½ tsp cinnamon
- ½ tsp nutmeg
- ½ tsp dry mustard
- 4 cups chicken stock

Heat the oil over a medium heat in a large frying pan. Sauté the garlic and onion until translucent and then add the chicken slices and cook until brown on all sides. Remove the contents of the pan and set aside. Place the chutney and spices in the pan and when hot add the stock; heat through, stirring constantly.

Return the chicken, garlic and onion to the sauce; reduce the heat and simmer for 15 minutes. Serve on a bed of hot rice.

•

# Chicken Enchiladas

**Serves: 4**

**Nutritional value per serving**

Calories: 343 | Fat: 9g | Carbohydrate: 39.8g
Protein: 24g | Dietary Fibre: 3.1g

## Ingredients

- 1 small tin condensed chicken soup
- 3 tbs skimmed milk
- 125g diced chicken breast
- ½ cup salsa
- 100g green chillies, diced

- 4 flour tortillas

Mix together the soup and milk in a mixing bowl. Combine the chicken, salsa, chillis and 2 tablespoons of the soup-milk mixture.

Spread about 2 tablespoons of chicken mixture on each tortilla, and roll up.

Place the tortillas in a lightly greased baking dish and spread the remaining soup-milk mix on top. Place in a preheated oven at 190ºC and bake for 30 minutes.

•

# Curry Chicken

## Serves: 4

### Nutritional value per serving

Calories: 145 Fat: 6g Carbohydrate: 19g

Protein: 19g Dietary Fibre: 3.6

## Ingredients

- 4 chicken breasts, skinned and boned
- 1 carrot, sliced
- 1 potato, chopped into 2cm pieces
- 3 tsp olive oil
- 1 onion, sliced
- 4 cloves garlic, thinly sliced
- 1 cup chicken stock
- 1 cup water
- 1 tbs mild or hot curry powder

Heat the oil in a large stainless steel saucepan, add the chicken breasts and cook on all sides until golden brown. Remove from the pan and place to one side.

Sauté the garlic and onion in the remaining oil until translucent. Stir in the curry powder for 1 minute then add the stock, carrots and potatoes.

When the stock begins to boil, return the chicken pieces to the saucepan. Cover and simmer over a medium heat for 40 minutes, or until the chicken and vegetables are cooked right through. Serve hot on a bed of rice.

•

# Mexican Chicken Breasts

**Serves: 4**

**Nutritional value per serving**

Calories: 170 | Fat: 2g | Carbohydrate: 9g
Protein: 27g | Dietary Fibre: 2g

## Ingredients

- 4 chicken breasts, boned and skinned
- 1 large onion, roughly chopped
- 1 green pepper, deseeded and roughly chopped
- ½ cup chicken stock
- salt and pepper for seasoning

Combine all the ingredients in a large stainless steel saucepan and bring to a boil over medium high heat. Lower the heat; cover and simmer for 15 minutes. Add more stock if necessary.

•

# Turkey Loaf

**Serves: 4**

**Nutrition Information Per Serving**

Calories: 260 | Fat: 13g | Carbohydrates: 9g
Protein: 26g | Dietary Fibre: 1g

## Ingredients

- 450g finely minced turkey breast
- 2 tbs olive oil
- 1 carrot, roughly chopped
- 1 onion, roughly chopped
- 1 green pepper, roughly chopped
- 150g button mushrooms, roughly chopped
- ½ tsp crushed dried thyme
- ½ cup breadcrumbs
- 2 tbs tomato purée
- 1 tsp Worcestershire sauce
- 2 egg whites
- 1 tsp mixed dried herbs

Combine all the vegetables, thyme, tomato purée, Worcestershire sauce, egg whites and mixed herbs in a mixing bowl.

Heat the oil in a large pan and cook the turkey meat until browned on all sides. Add the processed vegetables and cook over a medium heat, stirring frequently until the mixture is cooked through.

Stir in the breadcrumbs; continue cooking for a further 5 minutes; turn off the heat and allow cool for 10 minutes.

Form the mixture into a foil lined loaf tin. Bake in a preheated oven at 180ºC for 1 hour, or until nicely browned on top.

•

# Egg Noodles with Chicken Stir-fry

**Serves: 4**

**Nutrition Information Per Serving**

Calories: 237 Fat: 2g Carbohydrates: 39g

Protein: 18g Dietary Fibre: 0g

## Ingredients

225g skinless chicken breast, cut into strips
2 tbs olive oil
225g sweet potatoes cut into small cubes
1 bunch spring onions and tops, sliced
3 cloves garlic, sliced
2cm slice ginger root, thinly sliced
50g frozen peas
½ red pepper, roughly chopped
½ green pepper, roughly chopped
½ cup chicken stock
1 tsp light soy sauce
1½ tsp soy sauce
225g Chinese egg noodles, cooked

Using a large wok, heat the oil and stir-fry the strips of chicken breast until browned; then remove from the wok. Stir-fry the potatoes, spring onions, garlic and ginger root for 2 to 3 minutes; cover and continue cooking over a low heat until the potatoes are almost tender.

Add the peas and peppers to the wok; stir-fry over a medium heat until the peas are tender; then add the chicken.

Combine the stock, soy sauce and cornflour; add to the wok and heat to boiling; stir constantly until thickened. Serve whilst hot over the egg noodles.

•

## Chicken Breasts in Tomato Sauce

**Serves: 6**

**Nutritional value per serving**

Calories: 257 Fat: 11g Carbohydrate: 5g

Protein: 34g Dietary Fibre: 0g

### Ingredients

| |
|---|
| 6 medium size chicken breasts, boneless and skinless |
| black pepper for seasoning |
| 2 tbs plain flour |
| 2 tbs olive oil |
| 3 cloves garlic, crushed |
| 3 tbs dry white wine |
| 1 tbs chopped fresh rosemary |
| 6 plum tomatoes, diced |
| 4 tbs chicken stock |

Roll the chicken breasts in the flour then season with a dusting of black pepper. Heat the oil in a large frying pan over a medium-high heat. Add the chicken breasts and cook on both sides until lightly browned.

Place the chicken in an oven dish and bake in a preheated oven at 190ºC for 30 minutes. In a separate pan, cook the remaining ingredients over a medium heat until they boil. Turn down the heat and simmer, reducing the sauce to a thick consistency.

To serve, place chicken on a serving dish with the sauce poured over the top.

•

## Chicken Breasts in Rich Sauce

**Serves: 2**

**Nutritional value per serving**

Calories: 157 Fat: 2g Carbohydrate: 5g

Protein: 29g Dietary Fibre: 1g

### Ingredients

| |
|---|
| 1 tbs olive oil |
| 4 chicken breasts, skinned and boned |
| 1 tsp plain flour |

- 100g button mushrooms, sliced
- 1 tbs fresh lemon juice
- 100ml chicken stock
- 3 tbs dry Marsala wine

Dust the chicken breasts with the flour and brown in hot oil, turning often to ensure even cooking. Add the mushrooms and cook for 2 minutes.

Lower the heat to medium. Add the lemon juice, chicken stock and Marsala. Cover and simmer for 5 minutes. Transfer the chicken to a hot plate and keep warm.

Raise the heat to high and boil the liquid in the pan, stirring, until the sauce begins to reduce down. Return the chicken to the pan and turn to coat evenly. Serve immediately.

•

## Orange Chicken

**Serves: 4**

**Nutritional value per serving**

Calories: 206 | Fat: 2g | Carbohydrate: 16g

Protein: 30g | Dietary Fibre: 1g

### Ingredients

- 4 chicken breasts, boneless and skinless
- ¾ cup fresh orange juice
- 2 tbs low-sodium soy sauce
- 1 tbs brown sugar
- 1½ tbs cornflour
- 1 whole orange, peeled and sliced
- 2 tbs fresh parsley, torn

Arrange the chicken breasts in a single layer, top side up, in a baking dish.

In a small bowl combine orange juice, soy sauce, brown sugar and ginger. Pour over the chicken and bake in a preheated oven at 180°C for 35 minutes.

Remove the chicken from the pan. Combine the cornflour with half cup of cold water. Stir until smooth and then stir into the juices in the pan.

Put the chicken back into the pan and bake for a further 10-15 minutes or until the sauce has thickened and the chicken is tender when pierced with a fork.

When serving, garnish with orange slices and parsley.

•

# Fillet of Trout in Lime Juice

**Serves: 4**

**Nutritional value per serving**

Calories: 227 Fat: 8g Carbohydrate: 21g

Protein: 39g Dietary Fibre: 1g

## Ingredients

- 700g rainbow trout fillets
- 1 tbs lime juice
- ¼ tsp white pepper to season
- ¼ cup egg substitute
- ½ cup seasoned breadcrumbs
- 2 tbs sliced almonds

Combine the lime juice, white pepper and egg substitute in a mixing bowl. Dip the fillets in egg mixture and coat in breadcrumbs.

Arrange the fillets in a single layer in a greased baking dish and sprinkle with sliced almonds.

Cover and refrigerate for 1 hour.

Place in a preheated oven at 200°C for 10 minutes, until the filleted flesh is opaque and flakes easily with a fork.

•

# Roman Prawn Bisque

**Serves: 4**

**Nutritional value per serving**

Calories: 207 Fat: 4g Carbohydrate: 27g

Protein: 16g Dietary Fibre: 3g

## Ingredients

- 450ml prawns, peeled and coarsely chopped
- 2 tsp butter
- 2 tbs plain flour
- 2 cups chicken stock
- 2 cups skimmed milk
- 1 red onion, chopped

2 cooking tomatoes, deseeded
1 stick celery, sliced
1 tbs tomato paste
200g sweetcorn
2 tsp red wine vinegar
milled black pepper to taste

Melt the butter in a large saucepan over a medium heat. Add the flour and stir for 1 minute. Add the stock and milk and bring to a boil. Lower the heat and add the onion, tomato, celery and tomato paste. Continue simmering for a few minutes until the ingredients are combined.

Add the sweetcorn and prawns; then heat for a further 5 minutes until the prawns are cooked.

Add the vinegar and season with black pepper. Serve hot.

•

## Baked Salmon in Mustard

**Serves: 4**

**Nutritional value per serving**

Calories: 282 Fat: 17g Carbohydrate: 3g
Protein: 29g Dietary Fibre: 1g

### Ingredients

4 x 150g skinless salmon fillets
freshly ground black pepper

### Dressing

zest from 1 lemon
2 tbs olive oil
1 tbs dry breadcrumbs
1 tbs finely chopped parsley
2 tsp mustard seeds
juice of 1 lemon
1 tsp Dijon mustard

Combine all the ingredients except the salmon fillets and pepper in a mixing bowl and mix thoroughly.

Place the salmon fillets in a baking dish, skinned sides down and sprinkle with pepper. Spoon the mustard dressing over the fillets and bake in a preheated oven at 180°C for 35 minutes.

•

## Broiled Halibut Steaks

**Serves: 4**

**Nutritional value per serving**

Calories: 145 Fat: 3g Carbohydrate: 1g
Protein: 27g Dietary Fibre: 0g

### Ingredients

| |
|---|
| 4 x 2.5cm thick halibut steaks |
| 2 tsp olive oil |
| 2 tsp lemon juice |
| salt and black pepper for seasoning |
| 2 cloves garlic, crushed |
| 2 tsp dried mixed herbs |
| 4 fresh sprigs of rosemary |

Brush both sides of the halibut steaks with a mixture of olive oil and lemon juice; then season with salt and pepper.

Sprinkle the mixed herbs over the steaks and then place the steaks on the rack of a broiler pan.

Broil for 10 minutes, gently turning the steaks over halfway through broiling.

Serve the steaks with a sprig of rosemary placed on the top.

•

## Portuguese Baked Cod

**Serves: 4**

**Nutritional value per serving**

Calories: 536 Fat: 10.5g Carbohydrate: 9g
Protein: 96g Dietary Fibre: 2g

### Ingredients

| |
|---|
| 4 cod steaks, boned |
| ½ red onion, sliced |
| ½ red pepper, cut into thin strips |
| ½ green pepper, cut into thin strips |

2 celery stalks, cut into thin slices
1 tomato, sliced
2 cloves garlic, crushed
2 tbs olive oil
1 tbs concentrated tomato paste

Soak the cod steaks in iced water for half a day or longer. When ready pat dry; remove the skin and break into chunks.

Toss all the remaining ingredients in an ovenproof dish. Gently mix in the chunks of cod and cover with aluminium foil.

Bake in a preheated oven at 180°C for 1½ hours, or until the cod is soft and the flavours are blended.

•

# Garlic Prawns

**Serves: 4**

**Nutritional value per serving**

Calories: 172 Fat: 11g Carbohydrate: 3g
Protein: 15g Dietary Fibre: 0g

## Ingredients

2 tbs olive oil
4 cloves garlic, finely chopped
½ litre medium size prawns, peeled and washed
¼ cup dry white wine
1 tbs fresh lime juice
salt and black pepper for seasoning

Heat the olive oil in a large non-stick pan over a medium high heat. Sauté the garlic until translucent. Lower the heat; and cook for 1 minute longer, stirring to prevent the garlic from over-cooking.

Add the prawns to the pan and cook for 2 minutes, stirring occasionally.

Add the wine and lime juice; season with salt and pepper then continue cooking for a further 2 minutes or until the prawns are thoroughly cooked.

•

# Seafood Lasagna

**Serves: 4**

**Nutritional value per serving**

Calories: 351 Fat: 16g Carbohydrate: 32g
Protein: 22g Dietary Fibre: 1g

## Ingredients

- 100g prawns, cooked
- 100g scallops, cooked and sliced
- 100g crab meat, cooked and sliced
- 9 sheets lasagna pasta, uncooked
- 1 tbs olive oil
- 1 tbs plain flour
- 4 cloves garlic, crushed
- 1 cup skimmed milk
- 1 cup chicken stock
- ¼ tsp pepper
- 1 tsp dried basil
- 50g mozzarella cheese, shredded
- 5 spring onions, chopped
- 150ml low-fat cottage cheese
- 1 tbs dry white wine

Heat the oil in a large saucepan over a low heat. Add the garlic; stir in the flour; continue cooking and stirring constantly until bubbly. Remove from the heat and stir in the milk, stock and white wine.

Return to the stove and heat to boiling, stirring constantly. Boil for 1 minute; add mozzarella cheese, onions, basil and pepper. Cook over low heat until cheese is melted, stirring constantly.

Spread about 1½ cups of the sauce in an ungreased ovenproof pan. Cover with 3 lasagna sheets, overlapping as needed. Spread the cheese over the sheets. Spread with another 1½ cups of sauce and then top with another 3 lasagna sheets. Spread seafood over this layer and top with another 1½ cups of sauce. Cover with the last 3 lasagna sheets and top with all of the remaining sauce. If desired, top with grated parmesan cheese.

Bake, uncovered in a preheated oven at 180°C for 35 to 45 minutes or until the lasagna sheets are tender. Let stand for 15 minutes before cutting.

•

# Prawn Chowder

**Serves: 4**

**Nutrition Information Per Serving**

Calories: 240 | Fat: 3g | Carbohydrates: 25g

Protein: 30g | Fibre: 3g

## Ingredients

- 700ml cooked prawns
- 1 tbs olive oil
- 1 bunch spring onions, finely chopped
- 1 stalk celery, finely chopped
- 3 cloves garlic, crushed
- 700ml chicken stock
- 1 x 340g tin plum tomatoes
- 1 Charlotte potato, scrubbed and cut into thin julienne strips
- ½ tsp Italian herb seasoning
- freshly milled black pepper, to taste

Sauté the onion, celery and garlic in hot oil until translucent. Add the chicken stock, bring to the boil, then add all the remaining ingredients, except the prawns; reduce the heat and simmer, covered, for 15 minutes. Add the prawns and continue to simmer, uncovered, for another 5 minutes.

•

# Grilled Tuna Steaks

**Serves: 4**

**Nutritional value per serving**

Calories: 210 | Fat: 5g | Carbohydrate: 2g

Protein: 38g | Dietary Fibre: 1.5g

## Ingredients

- 4 tuna steaks
- juice of 1 lemon
- 1 tbs olive oil
- 2 cloves garlic, crushed
- 2 tsp chopped fresh oregano
- 1 tbs grated lemon zest
- ¼ tsp salt

Place the tuna steaks side by side on a dish that is suitable for placing in a refrigerator.

Whisk the remaining ingredients together to make a marinade. Pour the marinade over the fish and cover; marinate for 30-45 minutes in the refrigerator.

To cook, grill the steaks under a hot grill for 5 minutes each side to cook through. Baste the steaks with the marinade whilst grilling.

•

# Salmon Steaks with Hot Pepper Sauce

**Serves: 4**

**Nutritional value per serving**

| | | |
|---|---|---|
| Calories: 447 | Fat: 25g | Carbohydrate: 5.5g |
| Protein: 48g | Dietary Fibre: 1.5g | |

## Ingredients

- 4 salmon steaks
- 2 tbs olive oil
- 20g butter
- ½ tsp salt
- ¼ tsp freshly-ground black pepper
- 500g Chinese cabbage, sliced
- ½ tsp grated lemon peel
- 1 red pepper purée
- 1 tsp roasted red peppers, patted dry
- 1 tbs mild chunky salsa

Place the salmon steaks in a large heatproof dish; dot the butter and oil over the steaks and place in a preheated oven at 225°C for 5 minutes.

Remove the dish from the oven and season the steaks with salt and pepper. Bake for a further 10 minutes, turning carefully once halfway through cooking time, until just cooked through.

Remove the steaks from the pan and cover with aluminium foil to keep hot.

Place the Chinese cabbage sprinkled with lemon peel in the oven dish. Stir to coat with the juices and oil from the steaks. Place back in the oven for 1 minute, until the leaves are wilted and stems are warmed through.

Blend the peppers and salsa in a blender until combined and serve over the salmon steaks and cabbage.

•

# Italian Sea Bass Fillets

**Serves: 4**

**Nutritional value per serving**

| | | |
|---|---|---|
| Calories: 335 | Fat: 18g | Carbohydrate: 4.5g |
| Protein: 32g | Dietary Fibre: 1g | |

## Ingredients

- 700g sea bass fillets
- 1 tbs olive oil
- 1 small onion, chopped
- 10 olives, pitted, chopped
- 2 plum tomatoes, chopped
- 2 tbs capers
- 2 cloves garlic, crushed
- ½ cup dry red wine
- 1 pinch dried hot red pepper flakes
- 4 tbs butter

Heat oil in a large pan over medium heat until very hot. Add the onion and olives. Cook, stirring occasionally for 3 minutes, or until the onion is transparent. Add tomatoes, capers, garlic, wine and red pepper flakes. Bring to a boil; reduce heat and simmer for 5 minutes. Melt the butter in a large pan over a medium heat. Cook the fish fillets for 2 minutes per side or until lightly browned. Transfer the fillets to the tomato mixture, cover and cook over a medium heat for 3 to 4 minutes, just until the fish is cooked through.

•

# Danish Tuna

**Serves: 6**

**Nutritional value per serving**

| | | |
|---|---|---|
| Calories: 199 | Total Fat: 7g | Carbohydrate: 64g |
| Protein: 23g | Dietary Fibre: 4.5 | |

## Ingredients

- 1 large tin tuna in brine, drained
- 1 cup cabbage, finely chopped
- 3 tbs low-fat yoghurt
- 1 tbs tomato paste
- sprinkling ground pepper

| 6 slices bread, toasted |
| --- |
| sprinkling red pepper |
| 2 tbs vinegar |

Place the tune in a mixing bowl and flake the flesh with a fork. Mix in the cabbage and carrot; set aside.

Combine the yoghurt, tomato paste, vinegar and pepper, mixing well.

When ready, add the tuna to the yoghurt mixture and blend well with a fork.

Serve on toast with a side salad.

•

# Baked Scottish Salmon with Asparagus

**Serves: 4**

**Nutritional value per serving**

Calories: 246 Fat: 13g Carbohydrate: 6g

Protein: 26g Dietary Fibre: 2g

## Ingredients

| 4 salmon steaks |
| --- |
| salt and freshly milled black pepper |
| 3 tsp olive oil |
| 800g asparagus, topped and sliced into 5cm pieces |
| 6 spring onions, sliced into 5cm lengths |
| 1 tbs fresh lemon juice |
| 2 bay leaves, halved |

Place the salmon in the centre of a large double sheet of kitchen foil. Drizzle the oil over the top and place half a bay leaf on each salmon steak. Season well with salt and pepper.

Wrap the foil over the steaks to make loose but tightly sealed parcels. Place in a baking dish and cook in a preheated oven at 130°C for 1¼ hours.

Add the asparagus to a saucepan of boiling water and cook for 1 minute. Add the green onions and boil for a further minute then drain. Discard the bay leaves.

Serve the salmon steaks on individual plates with the vegetables to one side. Pour any juices from the baking dish over the asparagus and onions.

•

## Roast Salmon Fillets with Sweetcorn

**Serves: 2**

**Nutritional value per serving**

Calories: 186 | Fat: 13g | Carbohydrate: 16g
Protein: 19g | Sodium: 243mg | Dietary Fibre: 2g

### Ingredients

- 150g sweetcorn, fresh or frozen
- 150g salmon fillet, cut into 2 equal pieces
- 1 tbs plus 1 tsp fresh lime juice, divided
- 1 clove garlic, minced
- ½ tsp chilli powder
- ¼ tsp ground cumin
- pinch salt
- pinch black pepper
- 1 knob of margarine

Arrange the salmon fillets skin side down in a shallow 1 litre baking dish, greased with non-stick cooking spray. Pour 1 tablespoon lime juice over the fillets and marinate at room temperature for 10 minutes.

Combine the garlic, chilli powder, cumin, salt and pepper in a small bowl then pour over the salmon fillets. Roast the salmon fillets in a preheated oven at 220°C for 15 minutes, or until the salmon is opaque and flakes when tested with a fork.

Cook the sweetcorn in a steamer for 10 minutes, or until tender, and when ready toss the corn with a small knob of margarine. Serve the sweetcorn with the salmon.

•

## Rainbow Trout with Almonds

**Serves: 4**

**Nutritional value per serving**

Calories: 227 | Fat: 8g | Carbohydrates: 22g
Protein: 40g | Dietary Fibre: 1g

### Ingredients

- 750g rainbow trout fillets
- 1 tbs lemon juice
- sprinkling lemon pepper to taste
- ¼ cup egg substitute

| |
|---|
| ½ cup seasoned breadcrumbs |
| 2 tbs sliced almonds |

Spray a shallow ovenproof baking dish with cooking spray.

Combine lemon juice, lemon pepper and egg substitute in a small bowl, then dip the fillets in the mixture and coat with breadcrumbs.

Arrange the breaded fillets in a single layer in a baking dish and sprinkle with sliced almonds.

Cover and refrigerate until chilled.

Bake the fish fillets for 10 minutes in an oven preheated to 200ºC, or until the fish is opaque and flakes easily with a fork.

•

# Orange Waldorf Salad

**Serves: 4**

**Nutritional value per serving**

Calories: 145 Fat: 6 Carbohydrates: 23

Protein: 3 Dietary Fibre: 1g

## Ingredients

| |
|---|
| 4 oranges, peel and slice the segments |
| ¼ cup walnuts, toasted |
| 1 eating apple, chopped |
| pinch ground cinnamon |
| 1 stalk of celery, sliced |
| 1 little gem lettuce, chopped |
| 150ml plain low-fat yoghurt |

Combine all the ingredients in a salad bowl. Cover and chill in a refrigerator for 1 hour before serving.

•

# Mackerel Salad

**Serves: 4**

**Nutrition Information Per Serving**

Calories: 181 Fat: 14g Carbohydrates: 11g

Protein: 9.5g Dietary Fibre: 0g

### Ingredients

- 135g penne pasta
- 135g smoked mackerel fillets
- 1 medium size apple, diced
- 2 sticks of celery, chopped
- squeeze of lemon juice
- 1 small bulb of fennel, diced
- ground black pepper

Cook the penne in boiling water until tender. Flake the mackerel fillets into a small bowl and squeeze a little lemon juice over the top. Season with pepper.

Add the penne and the remaining ingredients to the fish and mix together. Use a low-calorie dressing when serving.

•

## Avocado Salad

**Serves: 4**

**Nutrition Information Per Serving**

Calories: 102 Fat: 7g Carbohydrates: 8g

Protein: 2g Dietary Fibre: Trace

### Ingredients

- 1 heart of romaine (cos) lettuce
- 1 small ripe avocado, peeled, stoned and diced
- zest and juice of 1 lemon
- 175g bean sprouts, washed
- 120g sweetcorn, cooked
- 50g button mushrooms, sliced

Place the diced avocado in a large bowl with the lemon juice and zest. Add the bean sprouts, sweetcorn and mushrooms and gently mix together.

Serve on a bed of lettuce leaves.

•

# Tuna and Penne Salad

**Serves: 4**

**Nutrition Information Per Serving**

Calories: 336 Fat: 3g Carbohydrates: 47
Protein: 32g Dietary Fibre: 1

## Ingredients

- 135g penne
- 1 x 200g tin tuna steaks, in brine
- 1 stick of celery, washed and thinly sliced
- 1 small head of broccoli, chopped small
- 25g seedless sultanas, washed
- squeeze of lemon juice
- low-calorie mayonnaise, as required

Cook the penne in boiling water until tender. Flake the tuna steaks and place in a bowl. Add the rest of the ingredients and mix together.

Gently fold the penne into the mixture. Squeeze a little lemon juice over the top and if required a small amount of low-fat mayonnaise.

•

# Egg and Tomato Salad

**Serves 4**

**Nutrition Information Per Serving**

Calories: 30 Fat: 6g Carbohydrates: 3g
Protein: 8g Dietary Fibre: 0g

## Ingredients

- a few lettuce leaves
- 4 salad tomatoes, sliced
- 4 spring onions, sliced
- 1 hard boiled egg, sliced
- ½ punnet of watercress
- ¼ cucumber, peeled and sliced
- ½ punnet mustard and cress
- 8 small radishes
- 1 tablespoon olive oil
- 1 tablespoon apple cider vinegar
- seasoning

Wash the vegetables and break the lettuce leaves into small pieces and put into a salad bowl, with the cress, etc. Mix the oil and vinegar and flavour with salt, pepper. Sprinkle over the salad; garnish with sliced egg.

•

## Fennel Salad

**Serves: 4**

**Nutritional value per serving**

Calories: 60
Fat: 3g
Carbohydrates: 7g
Protein: 2g
Dietary Fibre: Trace

### Ingredients

1 heart of romaine (cos) lettuce, sliced
1 fennel bulb, shredded
8 small cauliflower florets
1 red onion, sliced

### Dressing

juice of 1 lime
1 tbs olive oil
3 cloves garlic, finely chopped
¼ tsp ground pepper, fresh
¼ tsp paprika

Combine all the salad ingredients in a salad bowl.

Whisk the dressing ingredients in a mixing bowl and when combined sprinkle over the salad; toss just before serving.

•

## Orange and Basil Salad

**Serves: 6**

**Nutritional value per serving**

Calories: 117
Fat: 4g
Carbohydrate: 19g
Protein: 3g
Dietary Fibre: 6g

### Salad

1 heart of romaine (cos) lettuce, sliced
1 small bunch radicchio leaves, torn

3 large oranges, peeled, sliced crosswise, deseeded
1 bunch of fresh basil, chopped

### Dressing

3 tbs white wine vinegar
2 tbs olive oil
1 tsp honey
1 tsp fennel leaves, chopped
1 clove garlic, crushed
zest of 1 orange
fresh ground pepper and salt to season

Toss the romaine and radicchio leaves in a large serving bowl and then scatter the basil on top.

Whisk together all the ingredients for the dressing. Pour over the salad and top with sliced oranges.

•

## Fresh Fruit Salad

**Serves: 6**

**Nutritional value per serving**

Calories: 90 Fat: 0g Carbohydrate: 20g
Protein: 3g Dietary Fibre: 1g

### Ingredients

450g fresh carrots, peeled and shredded
1 crisp eating apple, peeled and sliced
50g seedless raisins
150g sour cream
2 tbs skimmed milk
1 tbs lime juice
1 tsp sweetener
1 small bunch basil, torn
1 small bunch fresh rocket leaves, torn

Combine all the salad ingredients (not the raisins) in a serving bowl.

Mix together the cream, milk, lime juice and sweetener and pour over the salad. Sprinkle the raisins over the salad and serve.

•

## Potato Salad with Chicken

**Serves: 4**

**Nutritional value per serving**

Calories: 264 Fat: 2g Carbohydrate: 30g
Protein: 31g Dietary Fibre: 4g

### Ingredients

450g skinless chicken breasts, cooked and chopped into small pieces
450g potatoes, cooked and diced
175g French beans, steamed
125g plum tomatoes, diced

### Dressing

1 x 150g carton fat-free sour cream
2 tbs low-fat mayonnaise
1 bunch of fresh dill, snipped into ½ cm pieces
1 tbs white wine vinegar
freshly ground black peppercorns, for seasoning

Toss the prepared salad ingredients together in a serving bowl.

Combine the dressing ingredients and place in a small serving bowl with a spoon for guests to help themselves.

•

## Chicken and Spinach Salad

**Serves: 2**

**Nutritional value per serving**

Calories: 155 Fat: 4g Carbohydrate: 10g
Protein: 30.2g Dietary Fibre: 1.7g

### Ingredients

150g fresh spinach
2 oranges, peeled and cut into chunks
200g cooked chicken breast, sliced into small chunks
150g fresh strawberries

### Dressing

- 2 tbs red wine vinegar
- 3 tsp orange juice
- 2 tsp olive oil
- ¼ tsp dry mustard

Mix dressing ingredients and refrigerate.

Wash the spinach and tear into bite size pieces. Add the oranges, chicken and strawberries.

Serve with dressing.

•

## Banana Chocolate Parfaits

**Serves: 4**

**Nutritional value per serving**

Calories: 138 Fat: 3g Carbohydrate: 25g

Protein: 4g Dietary Fibre: 2g

### Ingredients

- 250g low-fat chocolate mousse
- 2 medium size bananas, peeled
- squeeze of fresh lemon juice
- unsweetened cocoa powder, or sprinkling of cinnamon
- 25g chopped walnuts

Cut each banana into 4 pieces and sprinkle with lemon juice.

Place 2 banana slices in each of 4 dessert parfait glasses. Top each with an equal measure of mousse; then sprinkle with a little cocoa powder or cinnamon.

Sprinkle with walnuts and serve.

•

## Baked Peaches

**Serves: 4**

**Nutritional value per serving**

Calories: 327 Fat: 11g Carbohydrate: 57g

Protein: 3g Dietary Fibre: 4g

## Ingredients

4 medium size peaches, thinly sliced
50g redcurrants, hulled
2 tsp lemon juice
1 cup water
50g sugar, or equivalent sweetener
1 tsp cinnamon
1½ tbs cornflour

## Topping

2 tbs plain flour
¼ cup rolled oats
1 tbs brown sugar, or equivalent sweetener
2 tsp cinnamon
3 tbs olive oil

Place all the topping ingredients together in a bowl and mix to a smooth paste.

Combine the peaches and remaining ingredients in a stainless steel saucepan and cook, stirring occasionally, over a medium heat until the fruit thickens.

Pour the hot fruit into a casserole dish and sprinkle the topping over the peaches.

Bake in a preheated oven at 180ºC for 10 to 15 minutes, or until the peaches are bubbly and the topping is crisp and lightly browned.

•

# Orange Fruit Dip

**Serves: 2**

**Nutritional value per serving**

Calories: 90 Fat: 5g Carbohydrate: 6g
Protein: 5g Dietary Fibre: 0g

## Ingredients

225g reduced-fat cream cheese, softened
1 x 150g carton of plain non-fat yoghurt
1 tsp vanilla extract
grated zest and juice from 1 orange

Blend the cream cheese and yoghurt until smooth. Stir in the remaining ingredients.

Chill for 30 minutes in a refrigerator and serve with fresh fruit.

•

## Fruit Refresher

**Serves: 4**

**Nutrition Information Per Serving**

Calories: 45 | Fat: 0g | Carbohydrates: 10.8g
Protein: 0g | Dietary Fibre: 0g

### Ingredients

- 700ml unsweetened low-calorie apple juice
- 700ml unsweetened pineapple juice
- 2 tbs fresh lemon juice
- 3 cinnamon sticks

Mix all ingredients together in a saucepan. Heat until simmering over a low heat. Remove the cinnamon sticks. Serve chilled.

•

## Honey Melon and Grapefruit Cocktail

**Serves: 4**

**Nutrition Information Per Serving**

Calories: 66 | Fat: 0g | Carbohydrates: 26g
Protein: 4g | Dietary Fibre: 0g

### Ingredients

- 2 grapefruit, peeled and cut into segments
- ½ a medium sized cucumber, cut into matchsticks
- ½ a canteloupe melon, deseeded, skinned and cubed

Mix the grapefruit, cucumber and melon. Chill, serve in individual dishes.

•

## Strawberry Fiesta

**Serves: 4**

**Nutrition Information Per Serving**

Calories: 76 | Fat: 0g | Carbohydrates: 17g
Protein: 2g | Fibre: 0g

### Ingredients

- 5 cups strawberries
- 2 cups grape juice
- 6 tbs cornflour
- sweetener equal to 2 tsp sugar
- ¾ tsp lemon juice

Dissolve cornflour in juice using a wire whisk. Gently boil until clear, stirring often. Add the rest of the ingredients and cook until the strawberries are soft. Remove from heat and mash the strawberries with a potato masher. Chill in the refrigerator before using.

•

## Banana Milk Shake

**Serves: 2**

**Nutritional value per serving**

Calories: 76 Fat: Carbohydrate: 6g
Protein: 5g Dietary Fibre: 14g

### Ingredients

- 1 ripe banana
- 5 mint leaves
- 1 tsp vanilla extract
- 2 cups skimmed milk

Purée the banana in a blender, add the remaining ingredients and blend well. Serve from a tall glass jug into tall glasses.

•

## Mango Milk Shake

**Serves: 4**

**Nutritional value per serving**

Calories: 150 Fat: 0.5g Carbohydrate: 30g
Protein: 5g

### Ingredients

- 4 scoops vanilla ice cream

- 1 sliced ripe mango
- ½ cup skimmed milk
- 3 tbs milk powder

Place all the ingredients into a blender and whisk on high until combined.

Place 4 tall tumblers in the refrigerator for about 10 minutes.

Fill each tumbler with milk shake and then return to the refrigerator for five minutes before serving.

•

# Fruity Quesadillas

## Serves 8

**Nutritional value per ½ quesadilla serving**

Calories: 234 Fat: 8g Carbohydrate: 36g

Protein: 7g Dietary Fibre: 2g

## Ingredients

- 4 low-fat flour tortillas
- ½ cup light sour cream
- ¼ tsp vanilla extract
- 1 mango, peeled and diced into 2cm pieces
- 450g fresh strawberries, hulled and sliced into quarters
- 1 small Comice pear, cored and diced into 1cm pieces
- 1¼ tbs runny honey
- 1 tbs finely chopped fresh mint
- 1 cup shredded mozzarella cheese

Mix together the sour cream and vanilla. Place in the refrigerator to chill. Meanwhile, place the prepared fruits and chopped mint in a mixing bowl; drizzle the honey over the top and toss the fruits lightly so that they are all coated with honey.

Spread half the cheese on one side of each tortilla. Strain any excess liquid from the fruit and divide the fruit over the cheese-covered halves of tortillas; then top with the remaining cheese. Fold each tortilla closed. Place the tortillas under a hot grill and heat on both sides until golden brown. Cut each in half and serve with the sweetened sour cream.

•

# Fruit Sorbet

**Serves: 4**

**Nutritional value per serving**

Calories: 31 Fat: 0.3g Carbohydrate: 7.6g
Protein: 0.4g Dietary Fibre: 5g

## Ingredients

| |
|---|
| 150ml cold water |
| 150ml low-calorie sweetener |
| 4 tsp fresh lemon juice |
| 950g fresh or frozen raspberries |

Combine the water, sweetener and lemon juice; bring to the boil for 1 minute, then allow to cool to room temperature – about 15 minutes.

Press the raspberries through a sieve to remove the seeds, then purée in a food processor until smooth. Add the remaining ingredients and process until blended.

Pour into a freezer proof 20 x 20 x 5cm plastic container and freeze for at least 4 hours or overnight. When ready to serve, thaw at room temperature for about 15 minutes to soften slightly.

To make other delicious sorbets, make use of blackberries, melons and any other fruits when in season. Tropical fruits, such as pineapples, passion fruit and paw-paw are all delicious and have a similar number of calories.

•

# Galia Margaritas

**Serves: 6**

**Nutritional value per serving**

Calories: 134 Fat: 0.5g Carbohydrate: 18g
Protein: Trace Dietary Fibre: Trace

## Ingredients

| |
|---|
| 2 tsp sweetener |
| juice of 2 fresh limes |
| 1 galia melon, skinned, deseeded and cut in 5cm chunks |
| 2 tbs sweetener |
| ½ cup tequila |
| ¼ cup orange flavoured liqueur, such as Grand Marnier |
| 1 fresh lemon, cut into 6 slices |

Place 2 teaspoons of sweetener in a small dish. Rub the rim of the margarita glasses with a small amount of lime juice and then roll the rims of the glasses in sweetener to coat. Place prepared glasses in the refrigerator until ready to serve drinks.

Combine the lime juice, galia melon, 2 tablespoons sweetener, tequila and orange flavoured liqueur in a blender and process until smooth. Fill the blender with ice cubes and process until mixture is a slush consistency.

Fill prepared glasses with margaritas; garnish each glass with a slice of lemon and serve whilst still chilled.

•

## Tropical Fruit Dip

**Serves: 2**

**Nutritional value per tablespoon**

Calories: 15 | Fat: 0g | Carbohydrate: 2.5g

Protein: 0.5g | Dietary Fibre: 0g

### Ingredients

1 bottle low-calorie soft drink, pineapple or orange flavour

900g vanilla low-fat yoghurt

Combine the soft drink and the yoghurt in a food blender then serve as a dip with assorted fresh fruit.

•

## Creamy Chocolate Drink

**Serves: 2**

**Nutrition Information Per Serving**

Calories: 104 | Fat: 2g | Carbohydrates: 17g

Protein: 8g | Dietary Fibre: 0g

### Ingredients

3 cups skimmed milk

150ml half-fat cream

2 tbs unsweetened cocoa powder

sweetener, as required

¾ tsp ground cinnamon

Place a little cold milk in a mixing bowl; add the dry ingredients and stir until dissolved. Heat the remaining milk and cream and when boiling stir into the mixing bowl.

Serve whilst still hot in mugs or cups.

•

# Eggnog

**Serves: 4**

**Nutrition Information Per Serving**

| Calories: 79 | Fat: 1g | Carbohydrates: 10g |
|---|---|---|
| Protein: 6g | Dietary Fibre: 0g | |

## Ingredients

- 2 cups skimmed milk
- 2 tsp cornflour
- 1 tsp custard powder
- sweetener, as required
- 1 egg, beaten
- 1 tsp vanilla
- pinch of ground cinnamon
- pinch of ground nutmeg
- 1 tsp brandy extract

Mix the cornflour, vanilla and sweetener with 1 cup of milk; then heat in a small saucepan until boiling, stirring constantly.

Beat the eggs in a mixing bowl. Mix the remaining cold milk with the eggs and custard powder; then add to the milk in the saucepan. Cook over a medium heat until slightly thickened, stirring constantly.

Remove from the heat and stir in the brandy extract and cinnamon. Cool to room temperature before placint in a refrigerator; chill for 1 hour then serve sprinkled with nutmeg.

•

# Margarita Punch

**Serves: 10**

**Nutrition Information Per Serving**

| Calories: 87 | Fat: 0g | Carbohydrates: 23g |
|---|---|---|
| Protein: 0g | Dietary Fibre: 0g | |

### Ingredients

700ml cranberry drink light
200ml raspberry drink light
2 cups ice cubes
1 cup diet ginger
1 fresh lime, sliced

Combine the cranberry and raspberry drinks, stir in the ice cubes, ginger ale and sliced lime; garnish with fresh cranberries if desired.

•

## Cornish Oat Cakes

**Serves: 25**

**Nutritional value per cake**

Calories: 102 Fat: 4g Carbohydrate: 15g
Protein: 2g Dietary Fibre: 1g

### Ingredients

½ cup butter
¾ cup light brown sugar
100g self-rising flour
pinch of cinnamon
225g rolled oats
1 large egg, whisked
240ml skimmed milk
200g seedless raisins

Cream together the butter, egg and sugar in a mixing bowl.

Add together the flour, rolled oats and cinnamon; gently fold the egg mixture into the dry ingredients; add the milk, then the raisins; continue mixing until all the ingredients are combined.

Divide the mixture into 25 paper baking cups, place on a baking sheet and bake in a preheated oven at 180ºC for about 20 minutes or until golden brown.

•

# Scottish Oat Cakes

**Serves: 20**

**Nutritional value per cake**

Calories: 104 | Fat: 4g | Carbohydrate: 15g
Protein: 2g | Dietary Fibre: 1g

## Ingredients

- ½ cup reduced-fat margarine or light butter
- sweetener equivalent to 1 cup light brown sugar
- 3 tbs fat-free egg substitute
- 1 cup self-raising flour
- 1 cup quick-cooking oats
- ¾ tsp bicarbonate of soda
- ½ tsp baking powder
- ½ cup seedless raisins
- ½ cup chopped walnuts

Whisk the butter and sweetener to a smooth consistency. Add the egg substitute and vanilla extract and process until smooth. Gradually stir in the remaining ingredients.

Spoon the mixture onto a greased baking sheet to form 20 rounds, spacing them 30cm apart. Flatten each round slightly with the tip of a spoon.

Bake at 180°C for 20 minutes, or until golden brown.

•

# Chocolate Meringues

**Serves: 8**

**Nutritional value per serving**

Calories: 18 | Fat: 0.3g | Carbohydrate: 4g
Protein: trace | Dietary Fibre: 1.2g

## Ingredients

- ½ cup sugar
- ¼ cup ground almonds
- 1 tbs unsweetened cocoa
- 1 tsp cornflour
- 2 egg whites
- ¼ tsp. cream of tartar
- ½ tsp vanilla extract

Mix together 2 tablespoons of sugar with the ground almonds, cocoa and cornflour.

Break the eggs into a mixing bowl and whisk until frothy. Add the cream of tartar and vanilla extract; continue whisking until soft peaks form. Gradually add the remaining sugar. Continue whisking until stiff and shiny; then gently fold in the cocoa mixture.

Drop the mixture from a teaspoon onto a lightly greased baking sheet to form small mounds. Leave about 5cm between each mound.

Bake in a preheated oven at 120°C for 40 minutes.

Allow the meringues to cool completely before storing.

•

## Carrot Cake

**Serves: 8 slices**

**Nutritional value per slice**

Calories: 105 Fat: 2g Carbohydrate: 20g

Protein: 5g Dietary Fibre: 1g

### Ingredients

| |
|---|
| 2 large egg whites |
| 115g plain non-fat yoghurt |
| 3 tbs olive oil |
| 75g dark brown sugar |
| 2 tsp vanilla extract |
| 300g plain flour |
| 2 tsp baking powder |
| ½ tsp bicarbonate of soda |
| 1 tsp ground cinnamon |
| ½ tsp ground nutmeg |
| 110g carrots, grated |
| 35g raisins, washed |

Whisk together the egg whites, yoghurt, olive oil, brown sugar and vanilla in a large bowl.

Sift together the flour, baking powder, bicarbonate of soda, cinnamon and nutmeg. Gradually fold into the egg mixture, stirring with a metal spoon until well blended.

Stir the carrots and raisins into the cake mixture.

Grease a 22cm cake tin then dust with flour and tap out the excess. Spoon the cake mixture into the prepared cake tin, smoothing the top with the back of a spoon.

Bake in the centre of a preheated oven at 200ºC for 45 minutes, or until a knife inserted in the centre comes out clean.

Remove from the tin and cool on a rack for 10 minutes.

•

# Apple Cake

**Serves: 8 slices**

**Nutritional value per slice**

Calories: 137 Total Fat: 1.2g Carbohydrates: 28.5g

Protein: 3.5g Dietary Fibre: 1.5g

## Ingredients

- 150g plain flour
- 1 level tsp baking powder
- 1 level tsp bicarbonate of soda
- ½ tsp ground cinnamon
- ½ tsp ground nutmeg
- 1 tsp low-calorie sweetener
- 1 medium size cooking apple
- 2 large eggs
- 2 drops vanilla extract
- 1 tbs skimmed milk
- 25g raisins (washed)

Grease and line a 20cm x 10cm loaf tin. Sift together the flour, baking powder, bicarbonate of soda, cinnamon and nutmeg – set aside.

Beat the eggs until light and add the sweetener.

Combine the flour mixture, milk and egg mixture, folding together until smooth.

Grate the apple (including the skin) into the mixture and add the raisins.

Pour the mixture into the loaf tin and bake in a preheated oven at 180ºC for about an hour, or until a knife inserted into the cake comes out clean.

•

# Chocolate Sauce

**Serves: 12**

**Nutritional value per serving**

Calories: 12 Total Fat: 1.2g Cholesterol: 35mg

Carbohydrates: 2g Protein: Dietary Fibre: 0g

### Ingredients

- 2 tsp cornflour
- 125mg cocoa powder
- 500ml cold water
- Artificial sweetener equivalent to 8 tsp of sugar
- 2 tsp vanilla essence

Combine the cornflour and cocoa in a mixing bowl; pour in the cold water and whisk until well blended.

Pour the cocoa mixture into a stainless steel saucepan and cook over a low heat, stirring frequently until the mixture comes to a boil.

Turn the heat down to its lowest setting and keep stirring until the mixture thickens. Remove from the heat and stir in the sweetener and vanilla, then cover and allow to cool before using.

This sauce is delectable as a dessert topping over ice cream, sponge cake, or fresh pears and is superb as the base for chocolate drinks.

•

## Belgium Truffles

### Makes about 6 dozen truffles

**Nutritional value per serving**

Calories: 48 | Fat: 3g | Carbohydrate: 4.8g

Protein: 0.6g | Dietary Fibre: 0g

### Ingredients

- 75ml boiling water
- 40ml margarine, melted
- 150mg sweetener
- 250ml powdered skimmed milk
- 1 tsp lemon juice
- 500mg semi-sweet chocolate chips
- 50mg butter, softened
- 50ml strong coffee
- 250mg cocoa powder

Combine the water, margarine, sweetener, milk powder and lemon juice. Blend ingredients until thick and smooth then set aside.

Melt the chocolate chips in a heatproof basin immersed to halfway in hot water.

When melted remove from the heat and stir in the milk mixture, butter, coffee and cocoa powder; mix well.

Chill for about 2 hours, or until firm enough to handle. Form the semi solid chocolate into balls and roll in cocoa powder. Chill until the truffles are firm and then store in refrigerator until required.

•

## Chocolate Pie

**Serves: 8**

**Nutritional value per slice**

Calories: 173 | Total Fat: 9g | Carbohydrates: 17g
Protein: 6g | Dietary Fibre: 1.5g

### Ingredients

- 1 packet unflavoured gelatine
- 350ml skimmed milk
- 50ml cocoa powder
- 1 tbs cornflour
- 1 egg separated
- sweetener, equivalent to 10 tsp sugar
- 1 tsp vanilla
- 50mg skimmed milk powder
- 50ml cold water
- 22cm baked pie crust

Measure 50ml of milk into a bowl and stir in the gelatine. Let it stand for 5 minutes to soften.

Measure a further 250ml of milk into a heavy stainless steel saucepan; mix in the cocoa powder and whisk until well blended.

Cook over a medium heat to boiling point then reduce the heat and simmer for 5 minutes.

Stir together the cornflour, egg yolk and remaining 50ml milk. Blend into the cocoa mixture and continue cooking over a low heat until the mixture thickens.

Stir in the gelatine and sweetener until they dissolve. Remove from the heat and stir in the vanilla. Allow chilling until partially set.

Beat together the egg white, skimmed milk powder and cold water until stiff peaks form and then fold into the chilled chocolate mixture.

Spoon the chocolate mixture into a pie shell and chill in a refrigerator for a further 4 hours until set.

•

## Chocolate Cheesecake

**Serves: 12**

**Nutritional value per serving**

Calories: 202 Fat: 11.4g Carbohydrate: 15.7g

Protein: 10.6g Dietary Fibre: 0g

### Base

- 250g chocolate wafer crumbs
- 25g sweetener
- 25g margarine, melted

### Topping

- 500ml low-fat cottage cheese
- 250g light cream cheese, softened, cut into cubes
- 2 eggs
- 175ml low-fat sour cream
- 300g sweetener
- 125g unsweetened cocoa powder
- 1 tbs cornflour

Combine all the base ingredients. Press evenly onto the bottom of a 20cm spring-form tin. Bake at 160°C for 5 minutes.

Blend the cottage cheese until smooth. Add cream cheese and mix until blended. Add remaining ingredients and mix until smooth. Pour into the tin.

Place back in the oven and cook for 45 to 50 minutes or until the topping is firm around the edges and slightly soft in centre. When cooked, run a knife around edge of the cheesecake to loosen it from the pan. Leave to cool on a rack, then cover and chill.

Top with fresh raspberries and grated plain chocolate.

•

## Scottish Scones

**Makes 16 Scones**

**Nutritional value per serving**

Calories: 97 Fat: 3g Carbohydrate: 16g

Protein: 3g Dietary Fibre: 3.1

### Ingredients

1 cup unbleached all-purpose flour
1 cup whole-wheat flour
1 tsp baking powder
½ tsp salt
4 tbs butter
1 cup buttermilk
½ cup seedless raisins

Sift all the dry ingredients together in a large mixing bowl. Add the butter and mix it into the flour with your fingers. Add the buttermilk and raisins and knead into a soft dough.

Roll out the dough on a floured board until 2cm thick, then cut into 16 rounds with a pastry cutter.

Place the dough rounds on a greased baking sheet and bake in a preheated oven at 220°C for 15 to 20 minutes, or until golden brown.

Serve freshly cooked within 1 day of baking.

•

## Chive Biscuits

### Makes 8 biscuits

**Nutritional value per biscuit**

Calories: 100 Fat: 5g Carbohydrate: 13g
Protein: 2g Dietary Fibre: 0g

### Ingredients

1 cup plain flour
1 tsp baking powder
¼ tsp salt
45g margarine
2 tbs fresh chives, chopped
½ cup low-fat buttermilk
1 tbs skimmed milk

Mix the flour, baking powder and salt in a large mixing bowl until well blended. Knead in the margarine with the fingers; add the chives and blend. Finally, add the buttermilk, stirring until a light dough is formed.

Turn the dough onto a lightly floured surface and knead 3 to 4 times. When ready, roll the dough until about 2cm thick, then cut into 8 pieces.

Place the rolled pieces on a greased baking sheet; brush the tops with milk and bake in a preheated oven at 200°C for 15 minutes, or until lightly browned.

•

# Date Bread

## Serves: 16 slices

**Nutritional value per slice**

Calories: 142 Fat: 5g Carbohydrate: 24g

Protein: 2g Dietary Fibre: 1g

## Ingredients

- ½ cup diced dried dates
- ½ cup water
- 1½ cups plain flour
- 2 tbs chopped walnuts
- 1 tsp baking powder
- 1 tsp cinnamon
- 1 tsp ground nutmeg
- ¼ tsp salt
- ¾ cup firmly packed dark brown sugar
- ½ cup skimmed milk
- 2 tbs olive oil
- 1 egg
- 1 tsp vanilla extract
- 1 tsp granulated sugar, for topping

Place the dates in a stainless steel saucepan and just cover with water. Bring the water to the boil, turn off the heat, drain and leave to cool.

Place the flour, walnuts, baking powder, cinnamon, nutmeg and salt in a mixing bowl; stir to combine then make a well in the centre.

In a separate bowl, stir together the brown sugar, milk, oil, egg and vanilla, until well blended. Pour into the well of the flour mixture; stir until combined then add the dates and lightly stir to incorporate.

Pour the batter into a greased 22cm x 12cm loaf tin and bake in a preheated oven at 180°C for 35 minutes. Allow to cool on a rack before storing.

•

## Rice Biscuits

### Makes 10 biscuits

**Nutritional value per biscuit**

Calories: 70 | Fat: 3g | Carbohydrate: 12g

Protein: 1g | Dietary Fibre: 0g

### Ingredients

- 1 tbs golden syrup
- 2 tbs peanut butter
- 2 tbs chocolate chips
- 2½ cups puffed rice

Melt the syrup, peanut butter and chocolate chips in a stainless steel saucepan. Remove from the heat and stir in the puffed rice until thoroughly mixed.

Spread the mixture on a pastry board; allow to cool, then cut into 10 pieces.

•

## Bran Cakes

### Makes 12 cakes

**Nutritional value per cake**

Calories: 135 | Fat: 4g | Carbohydrate: 22g

Protein: 3g | Dietary Fibre: 1g

### Ingredients

- 2 cups raisin bran cereal
- 1 cup skimmed milk
- 3 tbs vegetable oil
- 1 egg
- 1¼ cups plain flour
- ¼ cup brown sugar
- 2½ tsp baking powder
- 1 tsp mixed spice

Combine the milk, cereal, oil and egg in a large mixing bowl and place to one side for at least five minutes. Combine the remaining dry ingredients adding the cereal mixture last of all. Stir together until all ingredients are moistened and combined.

Grease a 12 section patty tin and fill each hole to about ½ full. Bake in a preheated oven at 220°C for 15 to 20 minutes.

•

## Cheese Dip

**Serves: 16**

**Nutritional value per serving (2 tbs)**

Calories: 50 Fat: 1g Carbohydrate: 5g
Protein: 5g Dietary Fibre: 0g

### Ingredients

- 100g fat-free cream cheese
- 100g fat-free sour cream
- 50g fat-free mayonnaise
- 50g reduced-fat cheddar cheese, grated
- 1 chicken breast, cooked and chopped small
- 1 tsp Worcestershire sauce
- 2 cloves garlic, minced

Combine all the ingredients in a food processor and whisk until well blended. Serve with water biscuits or pitta bread.

•

## Crab Dip

**Serves: 6**

**Nutritional value per serving**

Calories: 45 Fat: 1g Carbohydrate: 5g
Protein: 3g Dietary Fibre: 1g

### Ingredients

- 100g fat-free mayonnaise
- 100g fat-free sour cream
- 200g flaked, cooked crabmeat
- small bunch chervil, chopped
- 3 spring onions, finely chopped
- ½ tsp finely shredded lemon peel
- 1 tsp lemon juice
- dash of cayenne pepper

Combine all the ingredients in a mixing bowl and refrigerate for 2 hours before using.

To make the dip more interesting when serving, save some of the crabmeat and sprinkle it over the dip, adding a sprig of parsley for decoration.

Serve with crudities of your choice.

•

## Artichoke Dip

**Serves 6**

**Nutritional value per serving**

Calories: 38 | Fat: 0g | Carbohydrate: 7g

Protein: 2g | Dietary Fibre: 1g

### Ingredients

225g cooked artichoke hearts, finely chopped
100g plain fat-free yoghurt
100g fat-free mayonnaise
¼ cup grated Parmesan cheese
2 tbs green chilli peppers, diced

Stir all the ingredients together in a mixing bowl.

Grease a 22cm round quiche dish with cooking spray. Spoon the mixture into the dish and bake in a preheated oven at 180ºC for 20 minutes.

Serve with a mixture of crudities made from peppers, cucumbers and carrots.

•

## Peppered Spinach Dip

**Serves: 8**

**Nutritional value per serving**

Calories: 33 | Fat: 2g | Carbohydrate: 3g

Protein: 2g | Dietary Fibre: 1g

### Ingredients

125g spinach, finely chopped
¾ cup low-fat sour cream
1 tbs red wine vinegar
1 tbs fresh mint, finely chopped
2 cloves garlic, crushed
8 water chestnuts, cooked and crushed

salt and cayenne pepper for seasoning

Combine the sour cream, vinegar, mint, garlic and water chestnuts; season with salt and cayenne pepper; blend well.

Add the spinach to the dressing, cover and refrigerate for 1 hour before serving.

•

## Couscous

**Serves: 2**

**Nutritional value per serving**

Calories: 238 | Fat: 1g | Carbohydrate: 47g

Protein: 10g | Dietary Fibre: 0g

### Ingredients

1 cup skimmed milk

½ cup couscous

20g butter

25g seedless raisins

Heat the milk in a small saucepan, stir in the butter and when blended, stir in the couscous and raisins. Cover and remove from the heat.

Allow the dish to cool for a few minutes before serving.

•

## Mango Fruit Cup

**Serves: 2**

**Nutritional value per serving**

Calories: 275 | Fat: 10g | Carbohydrate: 55g

Protein: 8g | Dietary Fibre: 8g

### Ingredients

1 peach, stoned and sliced

1 cup skimmed milk

150g plain low-fat yoghurt

¼ cup bran flakes

1 tsp vanilla extract

2 tsp sweetener

dash of cinnamon

Combine all the ingredients in a blender and process on medium speed until smooth.

Serve in dessert bowls with cinnamon sprinkled over the top.

•

# Savoury Risotto Patties

**Serves: 6**

**Nutritional value per serving**

Calories: 88 Fat: 2g Carbohydrate: 13g

Protein: 5g Dietary Fibre: 0g

## Ingredients

50g diced green chillies

25g diced pimentos

1½ cups precooked white basmati rice

1 egg substitute equivalents

2 tbs skimmed milk

¼ tsp cumin

1 dash salt and pepper

225g low-fat cheddar cheese

Combine the chillies, pimentos, rice, eggs, milk, cumin, salt, pepper and ½ cup of the cheese in a mixing bowl. Spoon the mixture evenly into a greased 12 compartment baking tin and sprinkle with the remaining cheese.

Bake in a preheated oven at 200°C for 15 minutes or until set. Carefully remove the patties from the tin, arrange on a serving dish and serve hot.

•

# Winter Porridge Oats

**Serves: 4**

**Nutritional value per serving**

Calories: 280 Fat: 6g Carbohydrate: 45g

Protein: 13g Dietary Fibre: 0g

### Ingredients

- 3 cups skimmed milk
- 1½ cups quick-cook porridge oats
- ⅓ cup seedless raisins
- 1 medium apple, unpeeled, cored, cubed
- 3 tbs toasted unsalted sunflower seeds
- sweetener equal to 2½ tsp sugar
- sprinkling of ground cinnamon

Combine all the ingredients (except the cinnamon) in a stainless steel saucepan and cook over a medium heat, stirring constantly until boiling. Reduce the heat and simmer for 2 to 3 minutes until thickened.

Spoon the porridge into breakfast bowls; then sprinkle with cinnamon.

•

## Polenta

**Serves: 6**

**Nutrition Information Per Serving**

| | | |
|---|---|---|
| Calories: 55 | Fat: 0.5 g | Carbohydrates: 11.7 g |
| Protein: 1.2 g | Dietary Fibre: 0g | |

### Ingredients

- 3 cups fresh water
- ¾ cup yellow cornmeal
- salt and pepper to season

Heat the water to boiling in a medium size saucepan; gradually stir in the cornmeal. Cook over a medium to medium-low heat, stirring constantly, until the polenta thickens enough to hold its shape but is still soft. Season to taste with salt and pepper.

•

## Moroccan Toast

**Serves: 3**

**Nutritional value per slice**

| | | |
|---|---|---|
| Calories: 92 | Fat: 1g | Carbohydrate: 17g |
| Protein: 4g | Dietary Fibre: 1g | |

## Ingredients

- ¼ cup fresh orange juice
- 2 large egg whites
- ½ tsp vanilla extract
- 6 slices day-old bread, thick cut
- 1 medium orange, peeled and cut into 6 wedges

Whisk together the orange juice, egg whites and vanilla in a large bowl. Coat the bread slices on both sides with the mixture and place them on a greased baking sheet.

Spoon any remaining mixture over the slices. Bake in a preheated oven at 180°C for 15 minutes, or until golden brown, turning once after 8 minutes.

Serve hot, garnished with orange wedges.

•

# Wholegrain French Toast

**Serves: 2**

**Nutritional value per serving**

| | | |
|---|---|---|
| Calories: 214 | Fat: 4g | Carbohydrate: 3g |
| Protein: 14g | Dietary Fibre: 4g | |

## Ingredients

- ½ cup liquid egg substitute
- ½ cup skimmed milk
- ¼ tsp vanilla extract
- ½ tsp ground cinnamon
- 1 tsp sweetener
- 4 slices wholegrain bread
- 2 tsp olive oil

Mix together the egg substitute, milk, vanilla, cinnamon and sweetener in a mixing bowl. Dip the bread in the mixture, coating both sides.

Heat the oil in a frying pan and cook the bread slices until both sides are brown.

Place the toast on a serving dish and serve immediately whilst hot.

•

# Banana Cinnamon Toast

**Serves: 4**

**Nutritional value per serving**

Calories: 115 Fat: 3g Carbohydrate: 17g

Protein: 6g Dietary Fibre: 1g

## Ingredients

4 slices whole grain bread, toasted
½ cup low-fat ricotta cheese
1 medium banana, peeled and sliced
ground cinnamon

Spread each slice of toasted bread with two tablespoons of ricotta cheese. Arrange the sliced banana on top of the cheese then sprinkle with ground cinnamon.

Place on a baking sheet and toast under the grill until the banana starts to bubble and lightly brown. Serve hot.

•

# Swiss Cheese Sandwich

**Serves: 4**

**Nutritional value per serving**

Calories: 550 Fat: 30g Carbohydrate: 43g

Protein: 23g Dietary Fibre: 5g

## Ingredients

1 tbs olive oil
1 red onion, finely sliced
½ tsp garlic salt
1 tsp lemon juice
sprinkling of ground nutmeg
225g low-fat cheddar cheese, thinly sliced
8 slices wholemeal bread

Sauté the onions in hot oil until translucent and then sprinkle lightly with garlic salt. Stir in the lemon juice and nutmeg.

Layer each slice of bread with slices of cheese and a portion of onion. Sandwich the filling with a slice of bread on top.

Toast under a hot grill, turning once, until golden brown.

•

## Mushrooms on Toast

**Serves: 2**

**Nutrition Information Per Serving**

Calories: 157
Fat: 9g
Carbohydrates: 15g
Protein: 4g
Dietary Fibre: 1g

### Ingredients

- 225g mushrooms
- 3 tbs skimmed milk
- 15g margarine
- 25g plain flour
- pepper, salt and nutmeg to season
- squeeze of lemon juice
- 2 slices wholemeal bread, toasted

Skin and wash the mushrooms; cook very gently with 1 tablespoon of milk and the margarine in a closely covered pan for 20-30 minutes. Blend the flour with the rest of the milk, add to the mushrooms and stir until boiling. Simmer for a few minutes longer.

Season with pepper and salt, nutmeg and lemon juice. Serve the mushrooms on hot crispy toast.

•

## Mushrooms and Onions on Toast

**Serves: 2**

**Nutrition Information Per Serving**

Calories: 259
Fat: 9g
Carbohydrates: 22g
Protein: 5g
Dietary Fibre: 1g

### Ingredients

- 2 slices wholemeal bread, toasted
- 225g mushrooms, sliced
- 15g margarine
- 2 small onions, peeled and chopped

Sauté the onions and mushrooms in hot margarine for 5 minutes. Serve them on hot crispy toast.

•

# Breakfast Omelette

**Serves: 2**

**Nutritional value per serving**

Calories: 96 Fat: 39g Carbohydrate: 3g

Protein: 11g Dietary Fibre: 0g

## Ingredients

1½ tsp olive oil
1 cup egg substitute
¼ cup minced lean ham
½ green pepper, chopped
½ onion, chopped
freshly-ground black pepper, to taste

Beat the eggs in a mixing bowl and add all the ingredients. Heat the oil in a frying pan and when hot cook the mixture until set.

Gently lift the edges of the omelette with a spatula and tilt the frying pan to allow any uncooked portion to flow underneath. Continue cooking until the eggs are firm, then transfer to serving dish.

•

# Greek Omelette

**Serves: 2**

**Nutritional value per serving**

Calories: 106 Fat: 3g Carbohydrate: 8g

Protein: 12g Dietary Fibre: 2g

## Ingredients

½ onion, chopped
handful torn spinach leaves
3 tomatoes, skinned
1 cup egg substitute
6 pitted olives, sliced
dash freshly-ground black pepper
2 tsp olive oil

Heat 1 teaspoon of the oil in a frying pan until hot. Sauté the onion in the oil until translucent. Add the spinach and tomato; toss briefly, then remove from the frying pan and transfer to a small bowl.

Combine the egg substitute with the olives and pepper in a mixing bowl. Heat the remaining oil in the frying pan over medium heat until hot. Add the egg mixture and cook until the eggs begin to set. Gently lift edges of omelette with a spatula and tilt the frying pan so that any uncooked portion flows underneath. When the egg mixture is set, spoon the vegetable mixture over half of the omelette. Loosen the omelette with a spatula and fold in half.

•

## Curried Turkey Sandwich

**Serves: 1**

**Nutrition Information Per Serving**

Calories: 179 | Fat: 1g | Carbohydrates: 30g

Protein: 7 | Dietary Fibre: 1g

### Ingredients

- 2 slices wholemeal bread
- 15g low-fat spread
- 1 slice cold turkey, chopped
- 1 tsp chutney
- squeeze of lemon juice
- 1 tsp curry paste

Mixed the low-fat spread, curry paste, lemon juice and chutney; then spread the mixture on both slices of bread. Add the turkey filling and sandwich between the slices of bread.

•

## Turkey Rolls

**Serves: 2**

**Nutritional value per serving**

Calories: 239 | Fat: 6g | Carbohydrate: 37g

Protein: 10g | Dietary Fibre: 3g

### Ingredients

- 1 tbs fat-free mayonnaise
- 1 tsp Dijon mustard

squeeze of lemon juice
pinch of dill
½ small red onion, sliced
2 tsp olive oil
75g button mushrooms, sliced
2 finger rolls, split
75g thinly sliced cooked turkey

Make a dressing by combining the mayonnaise, mustard, lemon juice and dill. Set aside.

Sauté the onion in hot oil until translucent, add the mushrooms and continue cooking until tender.

Sandwich the turkey slices in the finger rolls, add the onions and mushrooms, then spoon the dressing over the top.

•

# Chicken Sandwich

**Serves: 1**

**Nutrition Information Per Serving**

Calories: 160 Fat: 12g Carbohydrates: 30g
Protein: 11g Dietary Fibre: 1g

## Ingredients

2 slices wholemeal bread
15g low-calorie spread
slices of chicken breast, minced or cut very finely
several lettuce leaves, shredded
low-calorie mayonnaise
seasonings

Spread the bread with low-fat spread creamed with a little salt, cayenne and a small pinch of mustard. Add the chicken mixed with mayonnaise, add the lettuce and cut to shape.

•

# York Ham and Scrambled Eggs

**Serves: 4**

**Nutritional value per serving**

Calories: 147 | Fat: 9g | Carbohydrate: 2g
Protein: 13g | Dietary Fibre: 0g

## Ingredients

- 3 eggs
- 1 tbs skimmed milk
- 4 spring onions, finely chopped
- ¼ tsp cayenne pepper
- 1 tsp margarine
- 50g Yorkshire ham, off the bone, diced
- ½ green pepper, chopped small

Beat the eggs in a mixing bowl, add the milk, spring onion and seasoning.

Melt the margarine in a non-stick frying pan, sauté the ham and green pepper for 2 minutes; then add the egg mixture.

Cook, stirring gently, until the eggs are cooked through but still moist. Serve hot.

•

# Mango-Banana Mousse

**Serves: 3**

**Nutritional value per serving**

Calories: 185 | Fat: 1g | Carbohydrate: 46g
Protein: 2g | Dietary Fibre: 4g

## Ingredients

- 2 medium sized mangos, stoned and sliced
- 2 ripe bananas, sliced
- 300g vanilla low-fat yoghurt
- ½ cup ice cubes
- dash of ground cinnamon
- dash of ground nutmeg

Combine all the ingredients in a blender. Cover and blend until smooth.

•

# Raspberry Banana Tofu Shake

**Serves: 4**

**Nutritional value per serving**

Calories: 51 | Fat: 1g | Carbohydrate: 8g

Protein: 4g | Dietary Fibre: 2g

## Ingredients

- 125g packet unflavoured soft tofu
- 1 ripe banana, sliced
- 1 small tin raspberries, unsweetened
- 4 fresh cherries

Combine all the ingredients in a blender and blend until smooth. Serve in dessert bowls with a cherry on top.

•

# Californian Fruit Compote

**Serves: 6**

**Nutritional value per serving**

Calories: 180 | Fat: 6g | Carbohydrate: 35g

Protein: 2g | Dietary Fibre: 0g

## Ingredients

- 200g unsweetened shredded coconut
- sweetener equal to 1 tbs sugar
- 4 large seedless oranges, peeled and divided into segments
- 1 large tin pineapple chunks in juice, drained
- 1 small tin maraschino cherries, for garnish

Combine the coconut and sweetener in a mixing bowl. Arrange alternate layers of oranges and pineapple in a serving dish; then sprinkle each layer with the coconut/sweetener mixture.

Chill in a refrigerator for several hours and garnish with cherries before serving.

•

# Lemon Pudding

**Serves: 4**

**Nutritional value per serving**

Calories: 210 | Fat: 6g | Carbohydrate: 33g
Protein: 7g | Dietary Fibre: 0g

## Ingredients

½ cup sugar
1 large egg
1½ tbs butter, softened
2 tsp grated lemon zest
3 tbs plain flour
1 cup skimmed milk
juice of 1 lemon
3 large egg whites
castor sugar for dusting

Whisk together the sugar, whole egg, butter and lemon zest until the mixture is combined. Fold in the flour and stir until smooth. Mix in the milk and lemon juice. Whisk the egg whites until stiff and then gently fold into the egg-sugar mixture until completely incorporated.

Spoon the mixture into 4 greased 150g ramekins. Set them in a shallow baking dish and add enough hot water to come two-thirds of the way up the sides. Bake in a preheated oven at 180ºC for 30 minutes, or until browned and set. Serve warm or chilled, dusted with castor sugar before serving.

•

# Mississippi Mud Pie

**Serves: 4**

**Nutritional value per serving**

Calories: 349 | Fat: 19g | Carbohydrate: 47g
Protein: 3g | Dietary Fibre: 2g

## Ingredients

50g butter
35g unsweetened plain chocolate
1 large egg
sweetener equal to 150g sugar
1 tbs golden syrup

| |
|---|
| ½ tsp vanilla extract |
| 1 x 20cm pastry case |

Gently heat the butter and chocolate in a stainless steel saucepan, stirring all the time until melted and blended.

Lightly beat the eggs until light and frothy. Stir in the syrup and sugar.

Pour the filling into the pastry case and bake in a preheated oven at 180°C for 30 minutes.

•

## Lemon Torte

**Serves: 4**

**Nutritional value per serving**

Calories: 287 Fat: 15g Carbohydrate: 26

Protein: 12 Dietary Fibre: 0g

### Ingredients

| |
|---|
| 4 egg yolks |
| sweetener equal to 1 tbs sugar |
| 1 packet unflavoured gelatine |
| ¼ cup water |
| 150ml low-fat whipping cream |
| 2 tbs lemon juice |
| 1 tsp lemon peel, grated |
| 1 tsp vanilla |
| 1 loaf shape sponge cake |

Whisk the egg yolks until fluffy. Gradually add the sweetener; set aside. In a separate bowl, dissolve the gelatine in water and set in a pan of warm water. Set aside.

In a large bowl, beat the whipping cream till fluffy. Blend in the lemon juice, peel and vanilla. Add the gelatine; mix well. Add the egg mixture; blend well. Chill in a refrigerator to thicken. Slice the sponge cake lengthwise into thirds. Spread thickened topping on each layer, then on top of the cake. Return to the refrigerator to set.

•

# Hawaiian Sorbet

**Serves: 2**

**Nutritional value per serving**

Calories: 204 Fat: 0g Carbohydrate: 50

Protein: 1g Dietary Fibre: 1g

## Ingredients

- 4 tinned pineapple slices in own juice
- 4 scoops raspberry sorbet
- 4 tbs non-fat whipped topping

Place 1 slice of pineapple on each dessert plate. Using an ice cream scoop, scoop out 2 portions sorbet for each plate.

Top with twisted pineapple slices. Garnish with whipped topping and serve.

•

# Passion Fruit Cheesecake

**Serves: 6**

**Nutritional value per serving**

Calories: 289 Fat: 13g Carbohydrate: 34g

Protein: 5g Dietary Fibre: 0g

## Biscuit Base

- 125g ginger biscuits
- 1 tsp cinnamon
- 50g butter

Melt the butter; finely crush the biscuits and combine with the butter and cinnamon; mix well.

Line an 18cm x 28cm tin with aluminium foil. Cover the base of the tin with the crushed biscuits and flatten down hard; chill in a refrigerator while preparing the filling.

## Filling

- 250g low-fat cream cheese
- 125g low-fat cottage cheese
- ½ cup condensed milk
- 5 passion fruit

- sweetener equal to 100g castor sugar
- 150g low-fat cream

Beat cream cheese, (sieved) cottage cheese and condensed milk in a mixing bowl until very soft and creamy; gradually fold in the pulp from 4 passion fruits.

Beat half the cream until soft peaks form, fold into the cheese mixture, pour onto prepared base, refrigerate until set.

Decorate with remaining cream, spoon over extra passion fruit pulp, swirl into the cream. Cut into squares and serve.

•

# Lemon Sorbet

**Serves: 2**

**Nutritional value per serving**

Calories: 36 Fat: 0g Carbohydrate: 8g

Protein: 1g Dietary Fibre: 0g

## Ingredients

- 1 sachet unflavoured gelatine
- 2¼ cups water, divided
- sweetener equal to 3 tsp sugar
- juice from 1 freshly squeezed lemon
- 2 egg whites
- 2 tsp grated lemon peel

Sprinkle the gelatine over 1 cup of water; let it stand for 5 minutes to soften. Add ½ the sweetener. Cook over a low heat, stirring, until the gelatine and sugar have dissolved. Pour into a large bowl; add the remaining water and lemon juice. Chill in a refrigerator until thick.

Whisk the egg whites with the remaining sweetener until stiff but not dry. Fold into the syrup mixture with the lemon peel.

Pour into a freezer container; cover and freeze for 2 hours or until frozen around edges.

Spoon the mixture into a large bowl and beat until smooth. Return to the container, cover and freeze for 3 hours. Transfer to a bowl and beat again. Return to the container, cover and freeze until firm.

•

# Raspberry Fruit Sorbet

**Serves: 4**

**Nutritional value per serving**

| | | |
|---|---|---|
| Calories: 72 | Fat: 0g | Carbohydrate: 17g |
| Protein: 2g | Dietary Fibre: 2g | |

## Ingredients

| |
|---|
| 500g raspberries, hulled |
| zest of 1 lemon |
| juice of 1 lemon |
| 1 tbs raspberry conserve |

Place all the ingredients in a blender and process until smooth. Pour into a freezer container; cover and freeze for 2 hours or until frozen around edges.

Spoon the mixture into a large bowl and beat until smooth. Return to the container, cover and freeze for 3 hours. Transfer to a bowl and beat again. Return to the container, cover and freeze until firm.

•

# Comice Pear Dip

**Serves: 4**

**Nutritional value per serving**

| | | |
|---|---|---|
| Calories: 60 | Fat: 0g | Carbohydrate: 6g |
| Protein: 8g | Dietary Fibre: 0g | |

## Ingredients

| |
|---|
| 225g low-fat cream cheese |
| 1 tsp vanilla |
| 2 tbs reduced calorie syrup |
| 2 Comice pears, sliced |

Mix ingredients with a fork and serve with slices of Comice pear. Store remaining dip in refrigerator in sealed container.

•

# Apricot Mousse

**Serves: 4**

**Nutritional value per serving**

Calories: 84 | Fat: 2g | Carbohydrate: 12g

Protein: 6g | Dietary Fibre: 0g

## Ingredients

- 1 x 340g tin apricots in juice
- 1 cup soft tofu
- 2 tsp vanilla extract
- 2 tbs skimmed dry milk powder
- 2 egg whites, at room temperature
- fresh mint

Mix the tofu, apricots, vanilla and dry milk in a blender. Add some of the apricot water, if necessary, to process.

Whisk the egg whites until stiff. Place the apricot mixture in a medium size bowl and fold in the egg whites. Spoon the mousse into dessert glasses and garnish with fresh mint leaves. Chill before serving.

•

# Chocolate Mousse

**Serves: 6**

**Nutritional value per serving**

Calories: 220 | Fat: 15g | Carbohydrate: 18g

Protein: 4g | Dietary Fibre: 4g

## Ingredients

- 75g unsweetened chocolate
- 1 cup skimmed milk
- ¼ cup egg substitute
- sweetener equal to 3 tsp sugar
- 1 tsp cornflour
- 2 tbs Grand Marnier
- ½ cup low-fat whipping cream

Place the chocolate and milk in a medium size saucepan. Warm over a low heat until the chocolate melts. Stir together the egg substitute, sweetener, cornflour and Grand Marnier in a small mixing bowl, then add to the chocolate mixture, stirring constantly.

Cook over a medium heat while stirring constantly until the mixture begins to thicken. Pour into a blender and whisk for 20 seconds to make a more creamy texture.

Pour the mixture into a mixing bowl and cover. Refrigerate for two to three hours or until chilled. Whip the cream and fold into the chocolate mixture. Refrigerate overnight to set.

•

# Comice Pears in Rum Sauce

**Serves: 2**

**Nutritional value per serving**

Calories: 77
Fat: 0g
Carbohydrate: 18g
Protein: 0g
Dietary Fibre: 2g

## Ingredients

1 ripe Comice pear
½ cup fresh pineapple cubes
sweetener equal to 1 tsp sugar
2 tbs light rum
several mint leaves for garnish

Slice the pears in half and remove the core. Cut a thin slice from the rounded side of each half so that they will sit flat. Place them on 2 dessert plates.

Purée the pineapple, sweetener and rum together in a blender. Spoon the purée over the pears and garnish with mint leaves.

•

# Chocolate Silk Mousse

**Serves: 4**

**Nutritional value per serving**

Calories: 139
Fat: 5g
Carbohydrate: 20g
Protein: 4g
Dietary Fibre: 0g

## Ingredients

1 sachet unflavoured gelatine
¼ cup cold water

- sweetener equal to 4 tsp sugar
- 2 tbs unsweetened cocoa powder
- ¾ cup skimmed milk
- ½ cup part skimmed ricotta cheese
- 2 tbs vanilla extract
- 2 tbs rum extract
- 100ml low-fat whipped topping

Sprinkle the gelatine over the water and let stand for 2 minutes to soften. Heat the sweetener and cocoa in a small saucepan. Stir in the milk and cook over a medium heat, stirring constantly, until the mixture is very hot. Add the gelatine mixture, stirring until dissolved. Transfer mixture to a medium bowl and refrigerate until slightly cold, do not allow to gel.

Combine the ricotta cheese, vanilla and rum extract in a blender. Blend until smooth, then transfer to a small bowl. Add the whipped topping; stir until well combined. Gradually fold the ricotta mixture into the cocoa mixture. Chill in a refrigerator until set.

•

## Banana Milk Shake

**Serves: 4**

**Nutrition Information Per Serving**

Calories: 150 Fat: 1g Carbohydrates: 30g

Protein: 5g Dietary Fibre: 0g

### Ingredients

- 750g Swedish glacé ice-cream
- 1 sliced banana
- ½ cup skimmed milk
- 3 tbs vanilla flavoured milk powder

Place all the ingredients in a blender and whisk on medium-high until smooth. Pour into chilled glasses and serve.

•

# Mocha Risotto

**Serves: 4**

**Nutritional value per serving**

Calories: 317 Fat: 12g Carbohydrate: 45g
Protein: 9g Dietary Fibre: 1g

## Ingredients

- 125ml black coffee
- 750ml skimmed milk
- 130g pudding rice
- sweetener equal to 110g sugar
- 75g unsweetened plain chocolate, grated

Combine the coffee, milk, rice and sugar in a stainless steel saucepan. Simmer gently, uncovered, stirring often for about 40 minutes, or until the mixture is thickened and the rice is tender.

Stir in the chocolate and serve hot with cream.

•

# Spanish Fruit Compote

**Serves: 6**

**Nutritional value per serving**

Calories: 207 Fat: 1g Carbohydrate: 45g
Protein: 1g Dietary Fibre: 5g

## Ingredients

- 3 tbs tequila
- 3 tbs orange-flavoured liqueur
- 3 tbs orange marmalade
- juice of 1 lime
- 225g fresh strawberries, hulled and sliced
- 4 oranges, peeled, sectioned and cut into small pieces
- 1 small honeydew melon, rind and seeds removed and cut into small pieces
- 1 galia melon, rind and seeds removed and cut into small pieces

Combine the tequila, orange-flavoured liqueur, orange marmalade and lime juice in a mixing bowl; stir well to mix the ingredients. Add the fruits and gently stir to combine with the dressing.

Refrigerate for several hours to allow the flavours to blend.

•

## Florida Grapefruit

**Serves: 2**

**Nutrition Information Per Serving**

Calories: 47 | Fat: trace | Carbohydrates: 8g
Protein: 1g | Dietary Fibre: 1g

### Ingredients

- 1 Florida grapefruit, segmented
- 2 tablespoons white wine
- ¼ teaspoon ground nutmeg
- ¼ teaspoon ground cinnamon

Place the grapefruit segments and any juice in a serving bowl. Mix the wine and spices together in a non-metallic pan and warm slightly over a low heat.

Pour over the grapefruit. Cover and leave to marinate for at least 2 hours before serving.

•

## Cinnamon Pears

**Serves: 2**

**Nutrition Information Per Serving**

Calories: 139 | Fat: | Carbohydrates: 7g
Protein: 1g | Dietary Fibre: 1g

### Ingredients

- 100ml dry cider
- squeeze of lemon juice
- ½ tsp ground cinnamon
- pinch of nutmeg
- 2 ripe dessert pears, peeled, cored and sliced in half
- sweetener equal to 1 tsp sugar

Place the cider, spices, sweetener and a squeeze of lemon juice in a pan and bring to the boil, cover and simmer for 3 minutes.

Poach the pears in the cider for 20 minutes, or until soft. Serve the pears in dessert bowls with the cider marinade.

•

# Peach Buttermilk

**Serves: 4**

**Nutritional value per serving**

Calories: 108 Fat: 1g Carbohydrate: 20g
Protein: 4g Dietary Fibre: 0g

## Ingredients

- 350ml low-fat buttermilk
- 2 large peaches, chilled, peeled and cut into pieces
- sweetener, equal to 2 tsp brown sugar
- 200g fresh strawberries for garnish

Blend all the ingredients in a food processor until the peaches are puréed. Serve in chilled glasses, garnished with sliced, fresh strawberries.

•

# Apple Tea

**Serves: 4**

**Nutritional value per serving**

Calories: 76 Fat: 0.2g Carbohydrate: 26.2g
Protein: 0.1g Dietary Fibre: 0.3g

## Ingredients

- 700ml apple juice
- 15ml honey
- 4 sachets green tea

Place the apple juice and honey in a saucepan over a medium heat; bring to a rolling boil then remove from the heat.

Place one tea bag in each teacup. Pour the sweetened apple juice over the tea bag; allow to brew for 2 minutes or until the desired strength is attained.

•

# Coffee Punch with Ice Cream Floats

**Serves: 2**

**Nutritional value per serving**

Calories: 242 Fat: 20g Carbohydrate: 16g
Protein: 2g Dietary Fibre: 0.5g

## Ingredients

- 75ml strong cold coffee
- 75ml cream
- sweetener equal to 1 tsp sugar
- 160ml chocolate ice cream
- powdered instant coffee
- cinnamon

Mix the coffee, cream and sugar in a large serving bowl.

Cut the ice cream into large chunks and float the lumps on the surface of the coffee mixture.

Sprinkle with powdered coffee and cinnamon. Serve immediately in tall glasses with a serving of ice cream on the top.

•

# Herbal Iced Tea

**Serves: 4**

**Nutritional value per serving**

Calories: 77 Fat: 0.2g Carbohydrate: 19g
Protein: 0.1g Dietary Fibre: 0.2g

## Ingredients

- 2 sachets lemon ginger tea
- 2 sachets red ginger tea
- 2 cups unsweetened apple juice

Steep the sachets in 4 cups of boiling water for about 10 minutes. Discard the tea bags. Combine the tea with the apple juice and refrigerate when coolled. Serve over ice.

•

# Coffee Latte

**Serves: 2**

**Nutritional value per serving**

Calories: 109 Fat: 2.6g Carbohydrate: 13g
Protein: 8g Dietary Fibre: 0g

## Ingredients

470 ml skimmed milk
2 tsp instant coffee granules
sweetener equal to 2 tsp sugar
1 tbs hot water

Dissolve the coffee granules and sweetener in hot water. Gently pour in the milk and mix well. Chill before serving.

•

# Imitation Pina Colada

**Serves: 2**

**Nutritional value per serving**

Calories: 137 Fat: 1g Carbohydrate: 30g
Protein: 3g Dietary Fibre: 1g

## Ingredients

240g fresh chopped pineapples
120ml fresh milk
120ml water
sweetener as required
590ml rum extract
½ tsp coconut extract
4 ice cubes

Place everything except the water and ice cubes in a blender and process on medium-high. Add the ice cubes one at a time; then add the water. Chill before serving.

•

# Orange Fruit Drink

**Serves: 2**

**Nutritional value per serving**

Calories: 168 | Fat: 3g | Carbohydrate: 30g
Protein: 5g | Dietary Fibre: 0.6g

## Ingredients

- juice of 3 oranges
- 160ml milk
- 160ml water
- 1 tsp vanilla essence
- 4 ice cubes

Place all ingredients except the ice cubes into a blender; blend on medium-high; then add the ice cubes one by one until smooth. Serve immediately in tall glasses.

•

# Spiced Orange Tea

**Serves: 6**

**Nutritional value per serving**

Calories: 5 | Fat: 0g | Carbohydrate: 1g
Protein: Trace | Dietary Fibre: 0g

## Ingredients

- 6 tsp green tea
- dried orange peel from 1 orange
- 2 tsp ground cloves
- 2 tsp ground cinnamon

Mix all the ingredients in a large plastic bag. Store in an airtight container for several days for the tastes to blend before using. Brew the tea in the normal way according to the strength desired.

•

# Summer Strawberry Lemonade

**Serves: 4**

**Nutritional value per serving**

Calories: 65 Fat: 0.3g Carbohydrate: 17g
Protein: 1g Dietary Fibre: 1g

## Ingredients

| |
|---|
| 240ml quartered fresh strawberries |
| 160ml lemon juice, fresh or bottled |
| 630ml water |
| sweetener as required |
| ice cubes |

Blend the strawberries and lemon juice in a blender until smooth. Combine the strawberry mixture, water and sweetener in a large glass jug. Pour over ice cubes in tall glasses.

# Book Three

# Diabetic Family Meals

# Introduction

Quite often, someone who is on a diabetic diet makes food choices for other members of their family. This can sometimes lead to conflict if family members are not happy with the low sugar, low-fat regime that is often provided. To overcome these difficulties the following daily menus have been produced to provide healthy meals that all the family can enjoy, without becoming too concerned about the amount of sugar and fat served in the recipes.

Learning about some nutrition facts is important to maintain a healthy diet. To do this we should study the food pyramid guide and focus on foods at the base of the pyramid, whilst eating less of the food at the top. Foods such as grains, pasta, breads and rice are in the group at the bottom of the food pyramid and they should be made the basis of a healthy diet.

## THE FOOD PYRAMID GUIDE

The Food Pyramid Guide is printed overleaf with the permission of the U.S. Department of Agriculture and the U.S. Department of Health and Human Services.

The Food Pyramid Guide is designed for anyone over six years of age and shows a range of daily servings for each food group. In general, teenagers and very active adults should choose the higher numbers of servings; children and seniors should choose the lower numbers of servings.

## FATS

One fat exchange is based on a serving size containing 5g of fat, or 1 tsp margarine or oil.

1 Serving = 1 rasher of bacon or 1 tsp of oil

2 Servings = 1 tbs salad dressing, or 2 tbs light salad dressing plus 1 tbs light mayonnaise

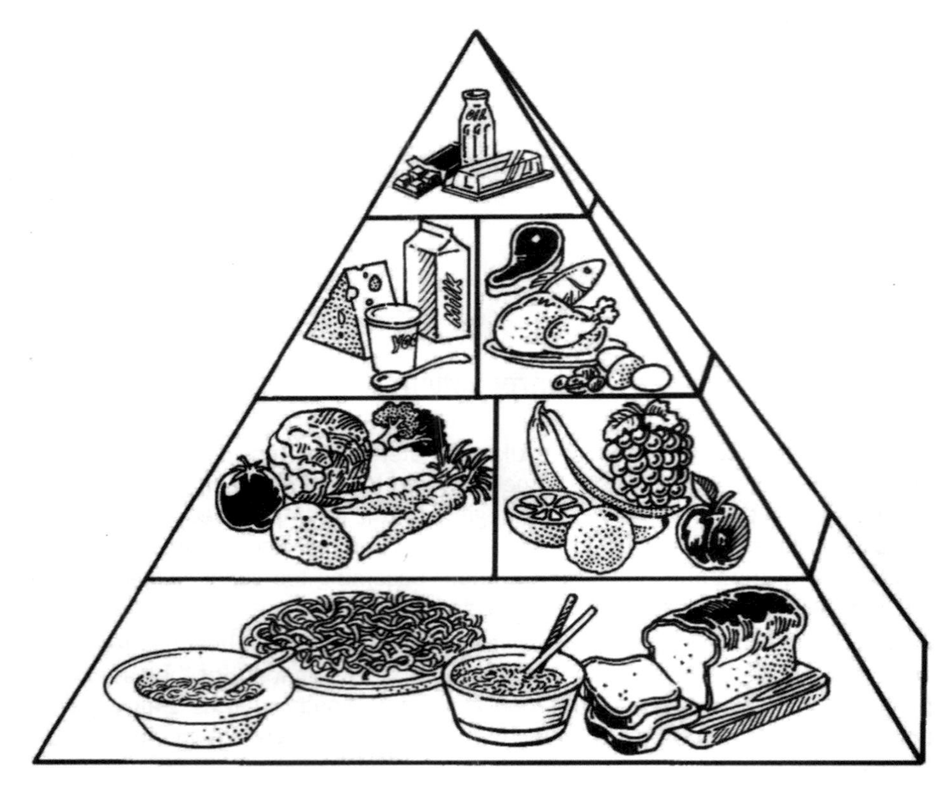

Fig 1 – The Food Pyramid

Food and drink that contain sugar – use sparingly. Dairy produce – 0 to 3 servings per day. Meals may include one or two servings of fat/oils.

As an alternative, use Soymilk – 1cup

Vegetarians who choose not to use milk, yoghurt or cheese need to select other food sources rich in calcium.

When drinking soymilk for the first time, consume a small amount in the first instance. If you suffer aches and pains similar to having the flu up to 24 hours later then discontinue; you may have an allergy to it.

Soymilk is a good alternative for children over two years old who do not like or are allergic to cows' milk. Soymilk comes in different flavours (you can add your own flavours if you like) and it's perfectly safe to give those to your child. Soy is also a good source of protein.

## VEGETABLES

One vegetable exchange = ½ cup of cooked vegetables or vegetable juice, or 1 cup of raw vegetables.

Eat a variety of vegetables – 3 to 5 servings a day comprising:

- Cooked or chopped raw vegetables – ½ cup
- Raw leafy vegetables – 1 cup
- Dry beans, nuts, seeds, egg and meat substitutes – 2 to 3 servings
- Cooked dry beans or peas – ½ cup

## FRUIT

One fruit exchange = 1 small to medium fresh fruit or ½ cup tinned or fresh fruit or juice.

Eat a variety of fruit – 2 to 4 servings a day comprising:

- Fruit juice – ¾ cup
- Chopped, raw fruit – ½ cup
- Tinned fruit – ½ cup
- Fruit, such as an apple, banana, or orange – 1 medium size piece.

## GRAINS

One starch exchange = ½ cup of cereal, grain, pasta, or starchy vegetable or 25g of bread.

You might need to eat one, two or three starch servings at a meal. If you need to eat more than one serving, choose several different starches or have two or three servings of one starch.

Bread, cereals, rice and pasta – 6 to 11 servings a day comprising:

- Bread – 1 slice
- Ready to eat cereals – 25g
- Cooked cereal – ½ cup
- Cooked rice, pasta, or other grains – ½ cup
- Bread roll – ½

Keeping these serving numbers in mind for each grouping can make a healthy diet easier to plan.

## PLANNING MEALS

Food choices are a key factor in managing insulin levels to achieve control of your blood sugar. Type 1 diabetics have to be aware of the action of the particular insulin product(s) they take and plan meals and snacks to avoid low blood sugar.

Type 2 diabetics may have to adjust from three standard meals each day to three lighter meals interspersed with snacks throughout the day, if necessary.

Experience shows that planning ahead is a good way to ensure that the right food choices are made to organise a balanced diabetic diet. The best way forward is to visit your doctor who will arrange for a nutritionist or dietician to design a meal plan that helps you control your particular type of diabetes, and one that fits into your lifestyle. Ideally, each meal should be based on a normal healthy diet that will satisfy all members of the family, and also fills a portion of your nutritional requirements over the course of an entire day.

It is sometimes easier to compile a menu to cover a whole week; in this way, we can choose foods from certain groups. For example, for breakfasts, bread, fresh fruit, cereals, fruit juice, milk and cheese can be chosen. In doing so, we can see that on any given day, we have a choice of one protein exchange, two starches, one fruit, and one milk. If cereals are chosen for breakfast, a piece of fruit, a glass of milk, and a small slice of cheese can also be included.

The following sample menus demonstrate how foods can be interchanged to create a balanced diabetic diet, whilst at the same time making those foods palatable for anyone with a healthy appetite to enjoy.

| **DAY ONE** | Calories | Fat | Carbohydrate | Protein | Dietary fibre |
|---|---|---|---|---|---|
| Nutritional values day one | 1222 | 19.1g | 162.9g | 77g | 4.6g |
| **Breakfast** | | | | | |
| Cornflakes with Skimmed Milk | 133 | 0g | 27g | 6g | 0g |
| York Ham and Scrambled Eggs | 147 | 9g | 2g | 13g | 0g |
| Tea with Skimmed Milk | 7 | 0g | 0g | 0g | 0g |
| **Lunch** | | | | | |
| Chicken Vegetable Soup | 260 | 4.1g | 29.9g | 24g | 0.6g |
| Orange Waldorf Salad | 145 | 6g | 23g | 3g | 1g |
| **Evening Meal** | | | | | |
| Mexican Pork Cutlets | 258 | 12g | 8g | 27g | 0g |
| Peach Pudding | 180 | 2g | 32g | 9g | 3g |
| **Snacks** | | | | | |
| Yoghurt Low-Fat | 112 | 1g | 22g | 5g | 0g |

| DAY TWO | Calories | Fat | Carbohydrate | Protein | Dietary fibre |
|---|---|---|---|---|---|
| Nutritional values day two | 1261 | 29.6g | 153.4g | 68.1g | 11.9g |
| **Breakfast** | | | | | |
| Dried Stewed Peaches | 77 | 0g | 27g | 1g | 1g |
| Banana Cinnamon Toast | 115 | 3g | 17g | 6g | 1g |
| **Lunch** | | | | | |
| Potato Salad with Chicken | 264 | 2g | 30g | 31g | 4g |
| Chocolate Cheesecake | 202 | 11.4g | 15.7g | 10.6g | 0g |
| **Evening Meal** | | | | | |
| Italian Vegetable Soup | 216 | 4g | 11g | 12g | 4.4g |
| Bread Roll, Baton | 182 | 1g | 38g | 6g | Trace |
| French Onion Pie | 68 | 4g | 7g | 2g | |
| **Snacks** | | | | | |
| Apple Cake | 137 | 1.2g | 28.5g | 3.5g | 1.5g |

| DAY THREE | Calories | Fat | Carbohydrate | Protein | Dietary fibre |
|---|---|---|---|---|---|
| Nutritional values day three | 1593 | 52g | 168g | 109g | 16g |
| **Breakfast** | | | | | |
| Tea with Skimmed Milk | 7 | 0g | 0g | 0g | 0g |
| Winter Porridge Oats | 280 | 6g | 45g | 13g | 0g |
| Wholegrain French Toast | 214 | 4g | 3g | 14g | 4g |
| **Lunch** | | | | | |
| Kedgeree | 495 | 24g | 31g | 44g | 0g |
| **Evening Meal** | | | | | |
| Baked French Fries | 93 | 3g | 15g | 2g | 1.8g |
| Chicken Breasts with Spinach Filling | 190 | 5g | 11g | 28g | 2g |
| Mango Fruit Cup | 275 | 10g | 55g | 8g | 8g |
| **Snacks** | | | | | |
| Café Noir Biscuit | 39 | Trace | 8g | Trace | 0g |

| DAY FOUR | Calories | Fat | Carbohydrate | Protein | Dietary fibre |
|---|---|---|---|---|---|
| Nutritional values day four | 1424 | 41g | 212g | 83g | 36g |
| **Breakfast** | | | | | |
| Tea with Skimmed Milk | 7 | 0g | 0g | 0g | 0g |
| Greek Omelette | 106 | 3g | 8g | 12g | 2g |
| **Lunch** | | | | | |
| African Vegetable Soup | 402 | 3g | 75g | 25g | 27g |
| Pitta Bread | 137 | 1g | 27g | 4g | 1g |
| Hummus Paste | 70 | 6g | 8g | 5g | 1g |
| **Evening Meal** | | | | | |
| French Lamb Stew | 287 | 9g | 21g | 30g | 3g |
| Mississippi Mud Pie | 349 | 19g | 47g | 3g | 2g |
| **Snacks** | | | | | |
| Honey Melon and Grapefruit Cocktail | 66 | 0g | 26g | 4g | 0g |

| DAY FIVE | Calories | Fat | Carbohydrate | Protein | Dietary fibre |
|---|---|---|---|---|---|
| Nutritional values day five | 1304 | 84.2g | 143.5g | 68.5g | 13.5g |
| **Breakfast** | | | | | |
| Prunes in Natural Juice | 79 | 0g | 20g | 1g | 1g |
| Yoghurt Low-Fat Plain | 70 | 1g | 9g | 6g | 0g |
| Breakfast Omelette | 96 | 39g | 3g | 11g | 0g |
| **Lunch** | | | | | |
| Cuban Meatball Tortillas | 340 | 19g | 28g | 19g | 4g |
| Orange and Basil Salad | 117 | 4g | 19g | 3g | 6g |
| **Evening Meal** | | | | | |
| German Stew | 178 | 5g | 20g | 13g | 1g |
| Lemon Torte | 287 | 15g | 26g | 12g | 0g |
| **Snacks** | | | | | |
| Apple Cake | 137 | 1.2g | 28.5g | 3.5g | 1.5g |

| DAY SIX | Calories | Fat | Carbohydrate | Protein | Dietary fibre |
|---|---|---|---|---|---|
| Nutritional values day six | 1504 | 52g | 181.5g | 75g | 12.9g |
| **Breakfast** | | | | | |
| Prunes in Natural Juice | 79 | 0g | 20g | 1g | 1g |
| Yoghurt Low-Fat Plain | 70 | 1g | 9g | 6g | 0g |
| Mushrooms and Onions on Toast | 259 | 9g | 22g | 5g | 1g |
| **Lunch** | | | | | |
| Chicken Sandwich | 160 | 12g | 30g | 11g | 1g |
| Italian Vegetable Soup | 216 | 4g | 11g | 12g | 4.4g |
| **Evening Meal** | | | | | |
| Spiced Vegetables from Pakistan | 69 | 1g | 15g | 2g | 3g |
| Salmon Steaks in Hot Pepper Sauce | 447 | 25g | 5.5g | 48g | 1.5g |
| Hawaiian Sorbet | 204 | 0g | 50g | 1g | 1g |
| | | | | | |

| DAY SEVEN | Calories | Fat | Carbohydrate | Protein | Dietary fibre |
|---|---|---|---|---|---|
| Nutritional values day seven | 1083 | 38g | 128.5g | 74g | 8.2g |
| **Breakfast** | | | | | |
| Sliced Mango | 97 | 0g | 24g | 1g | 1g |
| Moroccan Toast | 92 | 1g | 17g | 4g | 1g |
| Tea with Skimmed Milk | 7 | 0g | 0g | 0g | 0g |
| **Lunch** | | | | | |
| Egg and Tomato Salad | 30 | 6g | 3g | 8g | 0g |
| Mango Milk Shake | 150 | 0.5g | 30g | 5g | 0g |
| **Evening Meal** | | | | | |
| French Green Beans with Tomatoes | 123 | 4.3g | 20.5g | 4.5g | 2.2g |
| Salmon Steaks with Hot Pepper Sauce | 447 | 25g | 5.5g | 48g | 1.5g |
| **Snacks** | | | | | |
| Apple Cake | 137 | 1.2g | 28.5g | 3.5g | 1.5g |

More than half of all adult diabetics manage their diabetes with diet rather than insulin or oral hypoglycaemic agents. It is important for people with diabetes to apportion smaller meals throughout the day, and for some it is a good way to optimise control of their diabetes.

## POINTS TO REMEMBER

- Choose foods from all six food groups of the Food Pyramid Guide each day.
- Eat a wide variety of foods from each group to get all your vitamins and minerals.
- Eat enough starches, vegetables, fruits and low-fat milk and yoghurt.
- Eat smaller amounts of lower fat protein foods.
- Eat fewer fats, oils and sugary foods.
- In any meal plan, it is acceptable to leave out any of the essentials with a main meal and have them later as a snack.
- When making food exchanges, make sure the serving amounts are appropriate so that the exchanges are equal.
- When eating out, avoid foods with high fat and sugar levels. These are usually identified as cheese, or sugary toppings and sauces.
- A meal plan doesn't dictate which specific foods to eat for a meal, but it does indicate approximately what time to take the meal, which food groups to refer to when planning the meals menu, and identifies the number of servings to take from each food group.
- In general, you should follow the same guidelines for eating sensibly as everyone else. If you do this, you will find that planning your menus and selecting foods in the right amount is uncomplicated and not at all difficult.